Somebody Help
ME

Somebody Help ME

A self-help guide for young sufferers from
Myalgic Encephalomyelitis,
and their families.

Jill I Moss B.A. M.Ed.

Sunbow Books

First Published in 1995
by Sunbow Books:
Sunbow House, 5 Medland
Woughton Park,
Milton Keynes, MK6 3BH

Printed in England by NDC Print
Biggleswade. Bedfordshire.

Illustrations by Laura Downing
for Sunbow Books.

British Library Cataloguing-in-Publication Data.
A catalogue record of this book is available
from the British Library.

ISBN 0 9525783 0 1

Contents

Section One: Introducing ME

Section Two: What Is Happening To ME?

Section Three: Through The Forest

Section Four: Climbing The Mountain

Appendix

Acknowledgements

Writing this book has been a rewarding task. Many people have given me encouragement and support along the way but to mention everyone would take up far too many pages. However, in mentioning a few, I hope that the many will take my grateful thanks for their assistance and encouragement.

Firstly, back in 1991, five hundred anonymous young people filled in a questionnaire about their illness, ME. Without their heartfelt comments that were included on those forms, this book may not have been written. Their words are threaded throughout the text and I am most grateful to Dr E Dowsett and the ME Association for allowing me to use them.

My special thanks go to Kerry and Anna for permitting their recovery stories to be printed: to Annabel, David, Eve, Julia and Rachel for their personal thoughts and to Emma, Laura and Leanne for their delightful poems.

Some of the more technical chapters in Section Two have been seen by Dr Elizabeth Dowsett, Dr Charles Shepherd, Dr Colin Paton and Professor Horne. I am most grateful for their time and appreciative of their support.

The editing has been undertaken by my husband, John. While I invariably crept off to bed early, he would be left burning the midnight oil, trying to make sense of my latest chapter. Many thanks go to him. From the first small seeds of an idea, to the final publication of this book, he has continued to encourage and support me - as well as write all over my work in red pen!

On this theme, I am also indebted to Lynn Watling for the proof-reading - and more red pen!

I have no doubt that you will be enchanted by Laura Downing's illustrations. She has captured my thoughts perfectly and brought many aspects of ME to life through her drawings. My grateful thanks go to her for maintaining the flow of illustrations, always keeping up with demand and always producing something special.

Finally, I must mention my family and express my appreciation for their support. My three grown up children and their partners have always thought that this book was one of my better ideas!

Dedication

"Somebody Help ME" is dedicated to
all those young people who are presently
struggling with ME.

Your strength, patience and fortitude
are a lesson to us all.

Keep Smiling

Preface

"Go home and rest", said my consultant, "and don't do anything silly like have a game of squash!" Was he joking, or what? It had taken me five minutes to shuffle just ten metres down the corridor and into his surgery, and that leaning heavily on my husband's arm. There was certainly no chance of playing squash, or anything else come to that.

I was lucky, or so I was told. I had a G.P., and a consultant who beleived in ME and I was told to rest from the outset. However, I'm a person who never gives in without knowing the reason why and much of the advice that I was given only left me with more and more questions.

I read books, joined the ME organisations and soon picked up the general trend and felt supported in the fact that I was not the only one who felt so awful. Most of my questions were answered.

Very gradually my health improved and I began to miss the students and my colleagues at the school where I taught. Joining the local ME support group, I became friendly with four young people, aged between 10 and 17 years old. In my ignorance, I hadn't realised that young people were also affected. It seemed really hard luck to have ME at my age but to be a child or an adolescent with ME must be devastating. There you are on the brink of independence, when your peer group is so important, and you are developing a suitable self-image when suddenly the pain and utter fatigue of ME throws you back to a total dependence on others while your friends carry on regardless with their own lives.

How did these young people get answers to their questions? Did they read the same books as me? Did their friends still visit them, as mine did? Sadly no; their 'friends' had gradually stopped coming round and the books were only read by their mums, as everything written on ME, seemed to them geared to adults. Not wanting to further concern any of their family, they had kept any questions to themselves.

I tried hard to find a suitable book that was appropriate for their age, something that they could relate to and understand. I found nothing but my quest led me to Essex, where I was shown over five hundred questionnaires that had been filled in by young people with ME, in 1991. These were crammed with heartrending comments and questions about their illness and loss of friends, together with 'loud' frustrations over how to balance activity and rest.

Clearly, my four friends were not alone in feeling rather 'shut-out' as far as information on ME in young people was concerned.

I rang the local library and ordered all the relevant research papers on ME from around the world. I would attempt to put this information into user friendly terms in a book especially for young people. If I'm successful it may 'open the door' for some of them. I hope it does for you.

Jill I Moss
1995

My First Six Months

I haven't got 'flu
So why am I so blue?
Blood tests galore
I can take no more.

"It's all in your head"
So my GP said.
Pains in my body,
HELP ME SOMEBODY.

The psychiatrist was understanding
He didn't keep me dangling.
At last, someone who believed in me
The plug had been pulled out of me.

The ME people came to the rescue
Now I say a big 'thankyou'.
Because of their care,
I'm getting somewhere.

(Leanne aged 11 yrs)

Section One

Introducing

ME

1

Introduction

"Where is a book that I can read about my illness."
(Young Person [YP] 13 yrs old)

This quote jumped out at me when I was looking through about 500 questionnaires, that had been filled in by young people with ME back in 1991.

Dr Elizabeth Dowsett, President of the ME Association and Chair of the working group looking at young sufferers, had distributed these anonymous questionnaires to anyone who had ME as a young person under the age of 25 years, and to those who cared for them. A partial analysis of the results was presented in the Spring '91 edition of Perspectives, the magazine of the ME Association:

> *"...our first impression is that these moving, sometimes witty, sometimes heartbreaking accounts would provide the basis for a book."*   (Dr E. Dowsett "Perspectives")

You have just started to read that book. But there are several excellent books written on ME, why the need for another?

Look at the young man's quote at the top of the page. He wanted a book that he could understand and relate to. He did not want his mum or dad to know more about his illness than he did. He was a teenager now, he needed to feel that he had some control of his illness. He must have felt that the available books somehow did not reach out to him.

I hear many young people say that they only read the case histories and "mum reads the rest". To read of others suffering in a similar way to oneself, is comforting but it doesn't take you any further forward in understanding why you feel as you do.

This book sets out to give you that knowledge. It will explain the nature of the illness and the problems it brings to young people. It endeavours to answer some of the questions that may be nagging inside of you and suggests ways of coping with the physical and emotional traumas.

Understanding what causes ME and what possibly happens to your body is the first step towards having control of it.

"The doctor just said that she had ME, there was no cure but she would get better. We both need to know what to do."   *(Carer)*

"If I can understand what is happening to my body, perhaps I can explain it to my friends."   *(YP 17yrs)*

The difficulty with explaining about ME is where to place the emphasis. The range of disability that one can suffer is enormous. Some of you will be unable to sit up, or even feed yourself, whilst others of you are managing to attend school/ college. By nature, I am an optimist and I would like to fill the following pages with success stories but that would leave those of you who are presently very poorly, feeling left out and forgotten. Some young people, severely ill with ME, feel that because the emphasis is often placed on others who are walking about, that they may have something different.

"Why isn't there more written about severe ME? At first I didn't even know that I had the same illness as everyone else. I was in such pain, with severe headaches and hallucinations."   *(YP 17yrs)*

On the other hand:

> *"Some of the books that you read sound awful as they*
> *tell you how ill you're going to get."*   *(YP 13yrs)*

Everyone is different. When you read about someone severely ill, it does not mean that you will be similarly affected.

I will attempt to cover all aspects of the illness: physical, mental and emotional. You will read of possible reasons for your painful muscles and your brain refusing to function. Most important of all, I will give you suggestions on how to cope emotionally with ME. Beating this illness is like conquering a mountain. It's incredibly hard work, satisfying and the view from the top is great!

The Granite Mountain

Dr David Bell, a paediatrician in the USA who works extensively with ME patients, describes ME as:

> *"..a huge granite block in front of us, appearing impenetrable."*
> *(Disease of a Thousand Names. Bell)*

Researchers, he says, are looking for tunnels to explore in this granite block. They are searching for a cure.

I think I have seen this 'granite block'. It is a huge mountain that seemed to jump into the path of my life when I was looking the other way. Where did it come from? One minute life's pathway stretched out in front of me, the next, SMACK! This great mountain called ME blocked my path and hid the sun. Has this happened to you?

Using the analogy of a mountain, this book will help you to see that, whilst your way forward may seem blocked, there are ways over the mountain.

Road Block

I think I have seen this mountain. It seemed to jump into the path of
my life when I was looking the other way.

Road Block

"I've had to put my life on hold. It's no good thinking of the future or planning anything."   *(YP 18yrs)*

This young man clearly feels that his way is blocked. His hopes of going to University have been put on hold and he is bitterly disappointed and frustrated. Well-meaning comments only seem to add to the frustration:

"My aunt keeps saying - just concentrate on getting well. There's plenty of time to think about college."
                              (YP 19yrs)

The aunt is right, there is plenty of time to think about college. The college course will be waiting on the other side of this mountain but that doesn't help you with the frustration of wanting to be there <u>now</u>. Dealing with the disappointment and frustration is the first step towards getting better. If you just stay where you are, staring at the mountain, you will feel useless and inadequate.

"It's all so hopeless. I feel a great sense of uselessness. I really should be doing something to get better, but I can't. It's so frustrating."   *(YP 20yrs)*

You are doing something to get better: you are reading this book. By following some of the ideas which are put forward in the following chapters, you and others will be able to set simple, attainable goals between you.

In a mountain climbing situation, an outsider would not try to push a climber to go any faster up the mountain than he or she felt able. Unfortunately, with ME, there are many well-meaning friends and carers that quickly take over and encourage the patient to do too much.

> *"I get so angry, so frustrated at not being able to carry on with the life I had planned. I often shout at my Gran because she thinks I ought to be doing more to help myself."*   *(YP 16yrs)*

Only you as the patient will know how much of the mountain can be scaled at any one time. By reading this book you will understand the limitations that ME brings. You will feel more confident to tell others what you can manage and be able to set simple goals for your recovery.

If you don't discuss your limitations then you may have to accept goals set by someone else. That someone else may not understand ME and insist that, for example, twenty minutes sitting out of bed is best, when you know that ten minutes is all that you can manage. You go along with their suggestion and promptly overdo it.

So take a good look at this mountain called ME. Dr Bell says that it appears impenetrable and we know that it will take many years for the researchers to find the tunnels. The way ahead for us is over the top but it is rather daunting, after all we have no climbing experience! True, so we must learn as much as we can about the terrain and set out to conquer it in the knowledge that at times it may be difficult.

The aim of this book is to help you plan a careful route over the mountain. To climb it will take time and immense patience. You may lose your way occasionally, in a confusion of conflicting emotions. The chosen path may be too slippery and relapses of varying degrees are common. This will cause you to re-plan.

You are certain to need time to rest, maybe to recover from a set back. But, by attempting the climb, you will be doing something positive, you will not feel useless and you will succeed, as others have done.

Bit by Bit

Take this book, like the route over the mountain, bit by bit. Don't rush at it, use the chapters as markers to take regular rests and share the experience with others.

Remember that everyone is different and whilst you will find many of the words from the young people and their carers very similar to your own, there will be others that you do not recognise and perhaps make you feel uncomfortable. Don't skip them, give yourself a long breather and read on. To feel in control of this illness you will need to understand as much as possible.

*   *   *

The first section of this book will tell you why the illness is called ME and what symptoms can be expected - a general overview of the mountain.

The second section explains what may be happening in the body. We shall look at what may be causing our symptoms and what we may do to alleviate them.

The third section is intended to help everyone through the emotional trauma of ME.

"I feel that I'm lost deep in a dark, dark forest and there's no way out." **(YP 15yrs)**

This third section guides the way through the forest of emotions and difficulties that we find ourselves in. This will be likened to a forest growing at the foot of the mountain. We'll identify the 'trees' as we go through, thus making it less frightening.

The fourth section suggests a map which can be used to scale the mountain. The greater number of young people are in the 'convalescent stage' of ME, needing pointers on how to pace themselves.

"I feel a bit better, go out and then I do too much. It's up and down the whole time." **(YP 16yrs)**

Many of you, unless you are very poorly, will be struggling with education as you climb the mountain, and this will be covered.

The final chapter will give you a view from the top of the mountain. You will read of how other young people have learnt a great deal about themselves in conquering the ME mountain and are now being able to pick up the threads of their life again.

2

What's In A Name?

"My doctor said I had a post-viral fatigue. He wouldn't call it ME as he was not sure if he believed in it."
                                        (YP 15yrs)

"The specialist calls it Chronic Fatigue Syndrome but I think it's ME."   *(Carer of 15yr old)*

"My child has Post Viral Fatigue Syndrome, can she still join the ME group?"   *(Carer of 12yr old)*

Over the years, the illness ME has been known under many names. Dr David Bell calls it the 'Disease of a Thousand Names'. Around the end of the nineteenth century people suffering from fatigue and listlessness were diagnosed as having neurasthenia which is almost certainly the same condition that we now call ME. It is interesting to note that the famous nurse, Florence Nightingale on her return from the Crimean War lived a further forty years virtually housebound with neurasthenia. The symptoms haven't changed over the years but the diagnostic label has. In fact, this label tends to differ from one country to another. Americans for instance prefer to call it Chronic Fatigue and Immune Dysfunction Syndrome(CFIDS).

When international meetings take place, the general term Chronic Fatigue Syndrome (CFS) is used. Indeed, more or less all scientific and clinical investigators use this term. However, there are many illnesses that come under the umbrella term of CFS and not all are caused by viruses. Exposure to certain chemicals or a physical injury may give rise to CFS, all with similar symptoms to ME.

Dr Bell writes against the use of the term CFS:

> *"I think that few people really like the name Chronic Fatigue Syndrome, especially patients. It implies a benign (mild) condition of almost no importance in which people are tired, maybe bored, probably because they work too hard or are depressed."*   (Disease of a Thousand Names. Bell)

Although writing for the American market Dr Bell shows his liking for the term ME:

> *"I like the term Myalgic Encephalomyelitis used in the United Kingdom; it is a little harsh and somewhat technical, but there can be no doubt that it is a real disease."*

The term ME (described more fully later in this chapter) was first used in the mid 1950s following an outbreak of an infectious illness at the Royal Free Hospital in London. ME is now used in other parts of the world, including Australia and New Zealand. It is a term recognised by the World Health Organisation who classify it as a *"disease of the nervous system"*
          (International Classification of Diseases. No 10)

Early in 1992, the ME organisations asked the Department of Health to set up a Task Force of doctors and scientists who had a wide range of expertise in the field of ME. Their task was to make recommendations to the Department of Health on the clinical diagnosis and management of CFS/PVFS/ME. This Task Force used all three names but in their report they stated that:

"The merits of the term ME are that it emphasises the physical aspects of the condition and that it is familiar to patients and the general public." (Task Force Report. 1994)

So are all these abbreviated terms, CFS, PVFS, CFIDS, ME, describing the same illness?

Let us look at each of the terms, breaking down the words according to the Oxford English Dictionary.

Abbreviations and their meanings

* CFS - Chronic Fatigue Syndrome

Chronic	-	Persisting for a long time
Fatigue	-	Extreme tiredness after exertion
Syndrome	-	A group of symptoms

Chronic Fatigue - without the Syndrome - indicates that the patient has been feeling exhausted for an extended period, usually for longer than three months. Chronic Fatigue Syndrome (CFS) is fatigue that has lasted for many months or years, together with a group of other symptoms (syndrome). The diagnosis of CFS applies to many illnesses. One of these illnesses starts from a viral infection, and is known as Post Viral Fatigue Syndrome (PVFS).

* PVFS - Post Viral Fatigue Syndrome

Post	-	After
Viral	-	Caused by a virus
Fatigue	-	Extreme tiredness after exertion
Syndrome	-	A group of symptoms

After an attack on the body by a virus, one becomes fatigued.

This post viral fatigue is suffered by everyone. The two or three days of feeling low after a heavy cold is post viral fatigue. The longer term recovery period (usually around 6 months) following Glandular Fever is also post viral fatigue. If a collection of other symptoms are occurring at the same time - severe headaches, problems with co-ordination and speech, muscle pain, inability to stand bright lights or loud noises - then it becomes a post viral fatigue *syndrome*. If this illness persists for six months or more it is generally called ME.

Some doctors will use ME from the start, especially if the patient is still going down hill after three or four months, whilst others will continue to call it Post Viral Fatigue Syndrome.

* CFIDS - Chronic Fatigue / Immune Dysfunction Syndrome

Chronic	-	Persisting for a long time
Fatigue	-	Extreme tiredness after exertion
Immune	-	Protection from an infection
Dysfunction	-	Not working correctly
Syndrome	-	A group of symptoms

We will see in Chapter 4 how the immune system is thought to be at the centre of all our symptoms. All the muscle pain, together with problems in the brain and nervous system are all thought to stem from an immune system that is not working correctly. The term CFIDS, then, probably comes close to explaining what is happening but, like CFS, it does not seem to give the illness the importance that it deserves.

" *CFIDS is not a minor or benign illness due to the stresses and strains of life. It is a serious, debilitating disease that robs its victims of both their health and their dignity.*"

(Disease of a Thousand Names. Bell)

* ME - Myalgic Encephalomyelitis

Myalgic	-	Muscle
Encephalo	-	Brain
Myel	-	Spinal Cord
itis	-	Inflammation

In the late Spring of 1955, patients were admitted to the infectious disease unit of the Royal Free Hospital in London, with a fairly unremarkable infection - sore throat, enlarged lymph glands and a slight fever. Some had a gastric upset while others had marked dizziness. In all, 292 people fell ill and the hospital was forced to close for three months.

Interestingly, only 12 of the hospital patients were taken ill, the remaining 280 were doctors and nurses. Following their sudden illness - known as the Royal Free Disease - they had a short period of remission, where they began to feel better. It wasn't long, however, before they were complaining of extreme fatigue and acute muscle pain. Abnormalities were found in the workings of the brain and central nervous system, due to inflammation of the spinal cord. With the muscles (myalgia), brain (encephalo) and spinal cord (myel) all being involved, the diagnostic name became Myalgic Encephalomyelitis (ME). As the illness had started with a virus, the diagnosis could equally have been Post Viral Fatigue Syndrome. ME, then, is the same as PVFS.

Many of today's sufferers of ME have similar symptoms to the Royal Free outbreak with myalgic and encephalitic symptoms but some do not. About 20% of diagnosed ME patients do not, for example, have any muscle pain (*myalgia*) and very few show evidence of inflammation of the spinal cord (*myelitis*). You can see, therefore, that doctors are wary of diagnosing Myalgic Encephalomyelitis when fatigue is given as the main and sometimes the only symptom.

"I told my doctor that I was so tired all the time. It sounds stupid but because I was so tired, I forgot about all the other things that were going wrong. When she asked me how long I had been feeling like this I just said - ages."   *(YP 20yrs)*

I name this illness...

You can appreciate from the above quote, how difficult it can be for the doctor to make an accurate diagnosis, when 'tired all the time' is the only information that is received. ME is not just fatigue or even chronic fatigue.   In the same way that migraine is a particular and devastating headache, ME is a particular and devastating Chronic Fatigue Syndrome. There are many reasons for headaches and similarly there are many reasons for fatigue. It is important, therefore, that your doctor is given all the information about how you are feeling in order to give the correct diagnosis. This sounds obvious but it is sometimes so difficult to tell someone exactly how you feel when you are so exhausted.

Similarly, of course, we need the doctors to understand the very obvious symptoms of ME. Dr Shepherd points out that unless a doctor recognises these *"highly characteristic features"* then the wrong diagnosis may be made and the patient given inappropriate advice:

"Patients who complain of being "tired all the time" (TATT in medical shorthand), along with a seemingly endless list of unrelated symptoms constitutes a considerable diagnostic problem."   *(Living With ME. Shepherd)*

One interesting rheumatic disorder that arises with young people is Juvenile Fibromyalgia. It has several features which seem to overlap with ME and some doctors have suggested that, being so difficult to distinguish from severe ME, it could be the same illness.

"Analysis of symptom visual analog scales for these children would suggest that juvenile primary fibromyalgia syndrome and CFS in adolescents represent the same clinical entity."

(Juvenile Fibromyalgia and CFS. Bell)

Dr Shepherd explains that while there is no really effective treatment for Fibromyalgia:

"many patients seem to benefit from gradually increasing physical activity and small doses of antidepressant drugs."

(Living With ME. Shepherd)

The 'physical activity' in particular is not thought to be the best solution for treating ME until the patient is feeling much better - see Section Four. For a correct diagnosis to be given, therefore, it is up to both patient and doctor to have as much information as possible. Fibromyalgia may be very difficult to distinguish from ME but other lesser illnesses can also come under the umbrella of Chronic Fatigue Syndrome.

"It should be noted that there are many lesser illnesses associated with fatigue and tiredness which are not true ME. They may be the aftermath of glandular fever or surgery..... diabetes, asthma, anorexia, an accident or emotional trauma, family disruption or even abuse."

(Children With ME. Dr Franklin)

Until there is a laboratory test for ME, many doctors may feel more comfortable with the more general term of CFS. We must bear in mind, however, that ME/PVFS is just one of the *many* Chronic Fatigue Syndromes.

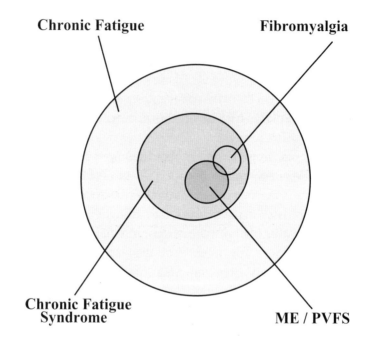

Myalgic Encephalomyelitis is just one of the
Chronic Fatigue Syndromes

3

This is ME

"It was a great relief to be actually told I <u>had</u> something <u>really</u> wrong with me."   *(YP 19yrs)*

"While an accurate diagnosis may not prevent medical complications and may not always offer relief of symptoms, it is essential for healthy, emotional development and long range educational planning."

(Disease of a Thousand Names. Bell)

Diagnosis

The illness ME has many severe and frightening symptoms. An early, accurate diagnosis is essential as it is easy to convince yourself that something much more sinister is happening.

"I was so relieved when I was told it was ME. There were times when I thought I was going to die."

(YP 17yrs)

However, a diagnosis is often a long time coming. I know the wait is frustrating but it is vital that the possibility of other illnesses that give similar symptoms to ME are eliminated first. Some of these can be cured quickly by suitable medication and some respond to a different management from ME. Be patient and keep calm.

Let's assume that you have an understanding doctor who is looking at all other possibilities and has indicated that you need to rest whilst tests are being carried out. You can expect, indeed you should hope for, many visits to your doctor, whilst the different blood tests are taken. Between visits it is helpful to keep a daily diary of symptoms. When you are suffering from extreme fatigue, regular headaches and tummy pains, it is easy to forget that your eyes hurt when you read or you can't bear to listen to the radio or to music. These smaller symptoms all add to the picture. Ask for this information to be kept with your medical records, it can be so useful for any discussions that you might come across later.

"I had written out a long list of her symptoms. I wish I had insisted that the doctor put the list in her file rather than hand it back to me. He understood but his replacement six months later did not."

(Carer of 15yr old)

You may be one of the unlucky ones who is or was faced with disbelief and misdiagnosis: perhaps even told that you are school phobic! I can only encourage you to remain calm and keep informing the professionals that you feel they have made a mistake. Compare your symptoms with the diagnostic criteria later in this chapter. Show this comparison to the doctor and/or the school and politely insist that they take notice of the contents.

Don't feel intimidated or angry as the doctor or educational officer may not even realise that ME can occur in children and young people. They may need you to educate them!

It is complicated in some respects by the fact that symptoms found in children are somewhat different from those in adults. Dr Bell explains that adults usually have two or three symptoms which remain their worst. For example, other than the usual overwhelming fatigue, my most severe symptoms are always muscle pain and headaches. For other adults it may be their inability to concentrate that is most severe:

> *"...but children may state that sore throat and headaches are the worst symptom one day, followed the next by lymphatic and abdominal pain being the worst."*
>
> *(Disease of a Thousand Names. Bell)*

To add to the complication, there are two patterns which generally show up with ME in young people:

1) Gradual *(Insidious)* Onset

2) Sudden *(Acute)* Onset

Dr Bell explains that although these two patterns of ME can be found in all ages, it is usual to find a gradual onset of symptoms occurring in children 5 to 12 years of age, whilst those with an acute onset of symptoms are usually in the adolescent age range.

The Younger Child

> *"I have rarely seen a sudden acute onset of CFIDS* (ME) *in a child younger than 10 years. Usually children from 5 to 10 years have a gradual onset of symptoms with periods where certain symptoms become more prominent."*
>
> *(Disease of a Thousand Names. Bell)*

The parent and child may have been backwards and forwards to the doctor with one minor symptom after another. A different symptom arises and a new infection is suspected but with careful questioning, Dr Bell often finds that all the symptoms have been present for a very long time.

"Young children who grow up with symptoms of CFIDS (ME) have become accustomed to these symptoms and are able to function well despite persistent and sometimes severe discomfort."   (Bell)

The problem for the parents is that if the young child has slowly got worse the youngster is often unable to explain how he or she feels, leaving the parents to guess.

"Paul went to school today but he still doesn't seem right. He didn't go out to play after coming home, so he can't be feeling 100%. Sometimes I wish he would complain and tell me how he feels and then I would know when he needs to be at home. Instead I have to wait until he is right off his feet." (Carer of 9 year old)

In the last chapter we saw how difficult it can be for a doctor to make a diagnosis when he or she is not given the full picture. So how can we be sure we have given the doctor the whole picture?

Dr Franklin, a consultant paediatrician in Essex recommends that Dr Bell's diagnostic criteria is followed for younger children.

DIAGNOSTIC CRITERIA FOR YOUNGER CHILDREN   (Bell)

Children should satisfy A and B to be given a diagnosis of CFS.

*   **A**: Symptoms present on a constant or intermittent basis for at least 6 months.

* **B**: Children should show at least 6 of the 8 major symptoms below:
    1) Fatigue
    2) Neurological complaints (difficulty in concentrating - could show as problems with learning)
    3) Headache
    4) Sore Throat
    5) Myalgia (muscle pain) and/or Arthralgia (joint pain)
    6) Abdominal pain
    7) Lymphatic pain or enlargement (Lymph glands at the front and back of the neck, armpit, groin)
    8) Disturbance of sleep pattern

OR   5 major symptoms above plus at least 2 of the following minor symptoms.
    1) Rash
    2) Chills/ Night Sweats
    3) General eye pain or sensitivity to light.

In my experience, young children also suffer from hyperactivity and disturbance of appetite. Responding to the information received from young people in their replies to the 1991 questionnaire, Dr Dowsett urged that these symptoms be included in relevant literature in order to prevent misdiagnosis of school phobia, behavioural disturbances and anorexia.

"Educational material issued by the ME Association to health professionals must make quite clear the essential variability of the energy deficit in children as well as their liability to periods of hyperactivity and gross mood and appetite disturbances."

(Report to ME Association from YP Working Party. 1991)

The Adolescent

With the older child, Dr Franklin follows a diagnostic criteria that is used by Dr David Lewis, consultant paediatrician in Aberystwyth. This scoring system is published in its complete form in the 1994 Task Force Report to the Department of Health, available from Westcare (see Useful Addresses). In addition, I have printed it separately in the Appendix for ease of photocopying.

Below is the scoring system used, although the words have been changed slightly to make them more user friendly.

DIAGNOSTIC CRITERIA FOR CHILDREN
(Task Force Report)

To be given a diagnosis of CFS the child must score 12 or more points from the list below.

Abnormal fatigue **must** be present.

* **Abnormal Fatigue -** to include (a) along with 2 others from (b)(c)(d)(e)
  (a) physical exhaustion which comes on within 12 hours of doing fairly simple activity and takes 24-72 hours to recover
  (b) exhausted but wanting to do more
  (c) waking from a night's sleep feeling exhausted
  (d) exhaustion accompanied by feeling unwell
  (e) tiredness or exhaustion which is made worse by any further infections such as the common cold.
  Score [5]

* Sudden onset which started with a feverish illness and/or sore throat and/or lymph glands enlargement (neck/armpit/groin). **Score [2]**

* Muscle pain and/or tenderness.   **Score [2]**
* Severe headaches which are not fully relieved by simple painkillers.   **Score [2]**

* Disturbance of temperature control (cold feet and hands with rest of the body feeling warm).   **Score [2]**

* Pins and needles / Feeling of being touched / Muscle twitching / Long term hiccup / Weakness or paralysis in fingers, hands or feet / Dizziness or feeling of losing one's balance (vertigo).
     Score [1] for each, using a maximum of 2 items

* Disturbance of memory / Difficulty with concentration / Inability to name common objects or calling objects by the wrong name
     Score [1] for each, using a maximum of 2 items

* Eye pain or blurring of vision after reading for more than 10 minutes / Oversensitivity to light / Oversensitivity to noise.
     Score [1] for each, using a maximum of 2 items

* Sleep pattern which is different from normal and on-going, day after day.   **Score [1]**

* Severe chest or tummy pains for most of the day over at least a month.   **Score [1]**

* Persistent change of bowel habit. Diarrhoea or constipation which is constant and different from normal. **Score [1]**

* Standing still considerably more tiring than walking.
                Score [1]

Dr Franklin also mentions in the Task Force report that the more severe forms of ME are probably more common in children than in adults, especially the neurological symptoms. In addition to those mentioned above these could be dizziness, mental confusion, unremitting headache, severe shaking episodes or what might seem like small fits without full loss of consciousness, difficulty in swallowing or talking.

To this list I would add the emotional mood swings, together with the unpredictability of symptoms. More often than not, these are seen as the most difficult symptoms to come to terms with.

"One minute I'd be laughing and joking and the next I'd be screaming and crying. If I tried to explain then they just said - but you were OK yesterday, I thought you were getting better."   *(YP 16yrs)*

Late Teens and Twenties

With this age, the illness and the presenting symptoms are similar to that of an adult. This leaves the well informed doctor with several diagnostic criteria to work from. Until recently the three most used case definitions were those developed in:

1) USA (Holmes 1988)
2) Britain (Sharpe 1991)
3) Australia (Lloyd & Hickie 1990)

The exciting news is that the doctors involved in these separate case definitions, Holmes, Sharpe and Hickie, together with over twenty others, are now working as an International Chronic Fatigue Syndrome Study Group and have published one comprehensive case definition which is printed opposite. I find it comforting to know that medical workers are combining their knowledge across continents.

The definition is short and to the point but, as with other definitions, it does define the larger circle - CFS - rather than the smaller one within it - ME/PVFS.

CDC CASE DEFINITION OF CHRONIC FATIGUE SYNDROME
(International CFS Study Group 1994)

A thorough medical history, physical examination, mental status examination and laboratory tests must be conducted before a diagnosis can be made.

A: **Fatigue**
Clinically evaluated, unexplained persistent or relapsing chronic fatigue that is of new or definite onset (i.e. not lifelong), is not the result of ongoing exertion, is not substantially alleviated by rest, and results in substantial reduction in previous levels of occupational, educational, social or personal activities.

B: **Symptoms** Four or more of the following are needed in addition to Fatigue.
1) Substantial impairment in short term memory or concentration
2) Sore throat
3) Tender lymph nodes
4) Muscle Pain
5) Multi-joint pain without joint swelling or redness
6) Headaches of a new type, pattern or severity
7) Unrefreshing sleep
8) Post-exertional malaise *(feeling very unwell after exercise or activity)* lasting more than 24 hours.

These symptoms must have persisted or recurred during six or more consecutive months of illness and must not have predated the fatigue (i.e the fatigue should not be as a result of the muscle pain, for example.)

It concerns me that 6 months of illness is still required before a diagnosis fits the criteria. I have seen many cases where young people have been very ill two or three months after a viral illness with clear ME symptoms. All the laboratory tests have come back negative and yet they are forced to wait in limbo land until the 6 months are up. It is hoped that the doctors are giving the diagnosis of PVFS at least, which doesn't have the term 'chronic' *(long term)* in its name. The advice should be to cut down on activity and to rest if the symptoms become worse. Don't be tempted to work the illness off while you are waiting for a diagnosis.

"At first I thought it was just a virus and I would get over it. I thought it was best to just keep going. I did all of my exams even though I felt really ill. I'm paying for it now. By doing this I have probably added years on to my recovery time."   *(YP 17yrs)*

*   *   *

If any of the three diagnostic criteria in this chapter indicates that you have ME, you would probably like to know:

* How many others are in a similar position?
* How long is it likely to last?
* How do others feel that have got this illness?

How Many Others?

You may recall that the motivation for writing this book was in response to the 500 questionnaires sent out in 1991 by the Working Party for young people with ME. These questionnaires were all read by Dr Dowsett and her team.

When this was completed, recommendations were made. One of these was to find out just how many young people suffered from ME.

Dr Dowsett, together with former Headteacher, Jane Colby, started in their home county of Essex. 18% of the schools that responded to that survey had cases of ME in their staff and/or their pupils.

The numbers of schoolchildren that had ME in Essex was then applied nationally revealing that 12,000 school children could be suffering from ME. Using this figure, the national average works out to be between 0.1% and 0.2% of the population.

Since the pilot study in Essex, Dowsett and Colby have extended their work to cover more counties and 12,000 now looks like a significant under estimate.

How Much Longer?

This is probably the most difficult question to answer in the whole of the book but naturally the one to which everyone wants an answer. The problem is that most published studies involve young people who were diagnosed in the eighties.

During this decade, it was difficult enough for adults to get an accurate diagnosis of ME and be given the correct management advice; it was almost impossible for young people. Many were diagnosed as being school phobic and in need of intensive exercise regimes.

These inaccurate diagnoses and the inappropriate advice that was given, probably put young patients' recovery back for months and even years.

From the 1991 questionnaires, Dr Dowsett picked up those young people who had been ill during the eighties and her findings showed an <u>average</u> length of illness of four and a half years.

I am confident that this figure will come down as diagnosis becomes easier and young people are allowed to rest from the onset of the illness. The good news is that youth is on your side. Whilst a complete recovery is sometimes thought to be difficult for adults, the majority of young people will get better: it will take time and bucket loads of patience but it will happen.

Those of you who feel that you have been in your present state of health forever should take comfort from this, although I know how difficult it is if you are taking a very long time to recover or are suffering from a relapse.

Relapse

ME is a fluctuating and unpredictable illness and there will be times when you may feel very poorly again. Some young people relapse into a worse state than when they were first diagnosed, often experiencing more pain and worse fatigue. For seemingly no reason, you can wake in the morning finding your symptoms much worse. With luck, a few days rest will improve things.

If you are not one of the lucky ones, your relapse may be much more severe. People around you will want to put a reason on this set-back and you may feel angry that they seem to care more about why it happened than how you feel at that moment.

However, they only want to prevent further relapses

happening and it is important for you all to take a look at any possible reasons.

The most common reasons for a relapse are:

* Another infection
* Undue stress
* Excessive physical or mental activity
* Immunisation
* Anaesthetics - general or local.

These reasons can often be discounted and if that is the case, then accept your relapse as an inevitable part of the illness.

"A few patients just seem to fall back into ill health for no apparent reason."   *(Living With ME. Shepherd)*

If you have kept a daily diary, then you will have a clearer idea of how long any previous relapses lasted and how you felt physically and emotionally during that time. If you are relying on memory then it is all too easy to think that the present relapse is longer and worse than the one before. Chapter 13 shows you how to put a numerical score to each day and graph the results across a page, so that the bad days are not seen as a step back but a step nearer to getting better.

Even those young people who never seem quite to hit that 'completely better' mark, are eventually able to return to school, college or work and generally enjoy life again.

"I'm better now, it's wonderful. I can even manage to play a set of tennis. OK, my friends can manage two sets but I'm nearly there."   *(YP 20yrs)*

It is important for you all to remain positive. Never give up hope. It will take time and I know the frustration of waiting but by following the suggestions of rest and gentle activity, the majority of you will recover and do all the things that you've ever wanted to do. Don't think in terms of "when will I be better" but rather, "what should I be doing to help myself to get better".

Remember that granite mountain that needs climbing? The important thing at the moment is to climb it carefully and safely - not to think about how quickly you can get over it.

How Do Others Feel?

Once a diagnosis has been made it is useful to contact others that feel the same as you. Joining a self-help group such as the ME Association's Young People's Group is a good place to start. Learning about what others can do or indeed cannot do, enables you to recognise your own capabilities.

The following two pages show a poem and some quotes from different young people when they were asked what ME meant to them. They show what a devastating illness it is. You may be tempted to pass over them quickly but it is important for you to know that there are others in the same boat as yourself, and some, perhaps, much worse. Again, of course, remember that everyone is different.

<u>Chances</u>

I feel that I haven't been alive long enough
To know what I need,
To know what my plan is,
To know from which influences to feed.

Now it is as if time has stood still
For me - but not for all.
Imprisoned in my body,
Balanced on the edge - poised to fall.

If I could have some idea of the outcome,
The time scale - it would be easier to bear.
I would know that I was doing right,
It would make life a bit more fair.

'Cos it seems if I were healthy
Life would be so easy to live.
I would know what I was up against,
I would know what I could give.

I want to know how this is affecting me.
I want to know if I'm still the same
But this illness will never let me.
It thinks it's all a game.

So the future is uncertain
But these are such precious years.
How come I feel I'm a bit too young
To be surrounded by these fears?

Laura (aged 15 years)

I can't even remember my own telephone number!

I stagger around as if I'm drunk

The doctors question me and I get very panicky.

I can't stand any more than one person talking at a time.

If I do manage to get out, I feel distant and out of touch. Like being in a dream - not part of it all.

I feel stupid. I always did very well at school, now I can't even spell simple words.
I feel I have nothing to offer anyone anymore.

For about four months I was so ill that I slept for 18-22 hours a day and could hardly get out of bed. I often just lay there waiting for mum to come home. When she did I'd just burst into tears.

I feel frightened of so many situations.   I used to be such a strong person.

My body feels alien from my brain.

Frustration is the hardest emotion to cope with.

My arms and legs feel like lead. They're sometimes very shaky.

I feel like an egg head. I talk gobbledegook. I know what I'm saying but no-one else knows!

I can start off walking with every one else and then I hit an invisible brick wall. I can't walk any further. Last week my dad had to back the car up this very narrow lane.
I was sitting in the gutter waiting for him.

My friends don't call anymore.They're all too busy getting on with their lives.
When will I be able to get on with mine?

Where Do I Fit In?

I'm sure many of you have been able to relate to some of the frustration that comes through in the poem and the quotes. Reading of how others feel about ME and the impact that it has had on their lives may help you to know that you're not alone but in some respects, it gives us more questions to answer.

* How long have they been ill?
* What are they able to do?
* Do they all feel the same pain as me?

Looking back at the diagnostic charts, none of them mentioned how bad the muscle pain had to be in order for you to score. Some of you will have constant and severe pain, whether you are at rest or trying to move around. Others of you will only notice it after you have walked too far or studied for too long.

In order to help you to find your level I have adapted an existing 'Disability Scale' into one especially for young people. It is modified from a scale that was sent out by the ME Organisations in 1994. It was a useful scale but was, I felt, rather confusing to follow. More importantly, it was written only for adults as there was no mention of schooling or even study at college.

Over thirty young people have assisted in the adaptation of this scale, giving me their opinions and where they thought they were on the scale.

"A scale like this is useful as I can show it to the doctor and say that I vary between 60% and 70% depending on the day."   *(YP 17yrs)*

To help us look positively at this illness, I have changed 'Disability Scale' into an 'Ability Scale'. Instead of appearing 70% disabled, I want you to think of yourself as 30% able.

Bear in mind that the scale is only a guideline. Space did not allow me to represent everyone. Some of you will fit in with one rating for physical abilities and another for mental tasks. I know of one young person who has recovered 95% physically, but is still having significant problems with learning. To be in this position raises problems with educational authorities when the child looks perfectly fit enough to return to school. Both physical and mental tasks sap the small amounts of available energy. If you give everything physically you will have difficulty with mental tasks. It's a balancing act and I have tried to reflect that in this scale.

I hope that by going up the ability ladder evenly, trying to balance out physical and mental tasks, you may be able to pace yourself more carefully and hopefully it will encourage you to see progress over the weeks and months. This scale is printed out again, without the comments, in the Appendix.

YOUNG PERSON'S ABILITY SCALE

100%   No symptoms even following physical or mental exertion. Able to study full time without difficulty, plus enjoy a social life.
> *"I'm fully recovered. I can play all sports and I've got a good job. I'm studying with the O.U. as I had to miss going to University at 18."*   *(YP 21yrs)*

95%   No symptoms at rest. Mild symptoms following physical or mental exertion - tire rather easily but fully recovered next day. Able to study full time without difficulty but it means a slight restriction on social life.

"In the main I have recovered. I am studying for three 'A' levels and I have a full social life. My only regret is that I don't have the energy to also take a Saturday job."   *(YP 18yrs)*

90%   No symptoms at rest. Mild symptoms following physical or mental exertion - tire easily. Study full time with some difficulty. Social life rather restricted.

"If I am really busy I feel more tired than my friends and I can't burn the candle at both ends like I could before. Going out with friends has to be kept to the weekends."   *(YP 20yrs)*

80%   Mild symptoms at rest, worsened by physical or mental exertion. Full time study at school or college difficult, especially if it is a crowded, noisy environment. Home tuition or part-time study without difficulty.

"My week is quite full but I have no energy left for socialising. When I get home from work I get a headache and my glands swell up."   *(YP 19yrs)*

70%   Mild symptoms at rest, worsened by physical or mental exertion. Daily activity limited.   Part time study at school/college tiring, restricting social life. With home study and careful pacing of activities, some social life is possible. Careful exercise may be possible: walking/swimming/cycling.

"Full time schooling would be far too tiring so I am studying hard at home in order to catch up with the others."   *(YP 13yrs)*

60%   Mild to moderate symptoms at rest. Increasing symptoms following physical or mental exertion. Daily activity very limited, although <u>gentle</u> walking, swimming or cycling is possible. Unable to study with others. 1 or 2 hours daily home study is possible. Quiet, non-active social life possible.

"I manage 2 hours of home study every day with no problem but full time education would be impossible. Walking upstairs is very difficult but I can manage about 400yds on the flat."   *(YP 14yrs)*

50%   Moderate symptoms at rest. Increasing symptoms following physical or mental exertion. Regular rest periods needed. Simple, short home study possible when alternated with quiet, non-active social life. Not confined to the house but unable to walk much further than 200yds. Enjoy a trip to the shops in the wheelchair.

"Have to shop in a wheelchair. I can manage one venue (e.g. library) if mum parks with my orange badge immediately outside."   *(YP 17yrs)*

40%   Moderate symptoms at rest. Moderate to severe symptoms following any physical or mental exertion. Not confined to the house but unable to walk much more than 100 or 200yds. Can manage a wheelchair outing to the shops on a quiet day. Requires three or four regular rest periods during the day. Only one large activity possible per day - friend dropping by <u>or</u> doctor's visit <u>or</u> short home study etc. Rest of the time spent pottering around.

"Most days I go for a short walk to the shops - 10mins there, rest and 10mins back. On the days that I go to physio that is all I do as it is very tiring. Other days I might have a friend around for an hour." (YP 16yrs)

30%   Moderate to severe symptoms at rest with possible weakness in hands and arms. Severe symptoms following any physical or mental exertion. Usually confined to the house but enjoy a quiet wheelchair ride or a gentle walk in the fresh air. Most of the day resting, although some small tasks possible (e.g. letter writing). Mental concentration poor and home study very difficult indeed.

> *"I get a lot of pain still but I enjoy writing letters to my friends and tackling an easy crossword."*   (YP 19yrs)

20%   Fairly severe symptoms at rest. Weakness in hands, arms or legs may be restricting movement. Unable to leave the house except rarely. Confined to bed/settee most of the day but able to sit in a chair for short periods. Unable to concentrate for more than one hour a day.

> *"I can sit in the wheelchair for an hour or two a day now. I go in the kitchen and watch the dinner being made. When I can sit in the chair without too much pain I'll go for a ride."*   (YP 16yrs)

10%   Severe symptoms at rest. In bed the majority of the time. No travel outside the house. Concentration very difficult indeed.

> *"I read a bit but I forget what I'm reading. With help, I can just get to the bathroom but if I go downstairs, mum has to carry me back again."*   (YP 14yrs)
> *"She can eat toast or sandwiches herself but nothing with a knife and fork."*   (Carer of 9yr old)

0%   Severe symptoms on a continuous basis. In bed constantly. Unable to sit up. Unable to care for yourself.

> *"I have to do everything for her. She has to lie flat with the curtains closed because her shoulders and neck are so painful and the light hurts her eyes. Until a few weeks ago she had to be fed with a tube as she was unable to swallow."*   (Carer of 14yr old)

ME then, is an extremely varied illness. Some of you will have spent some considerable time between 0% and 30%, whilst others have never dropped below 50%.

Whatever level you are on at the moment you must be wondering what is happening to your body to make you feel so ill.

The next section of the book gives you some idea about what may be happening.

Section Two

What Is Happening to ME?

4

The Immune System

Perhaps section two should be entitled:

"What **May** Be Happening To ME"

because until all the research is completed we must continue to live in terms of 'maybe'. We have seen that the term ME originated from an outbreak at the Royal Free Hospital in 1955 and since that time research work has increased. You can be assured that there are many people searching for the cause of ME.

The general opinion in the medical literature is that the illness is caused by a viral infection, although no one particular virus has yet been identified. What is not clear is whether the virus ever goes away completely or just hides away in body cells and reactivates from time to time.

Our body has an immune system which is supposed to protect us from microbes; does it not work? After all, the Americans call ME the Chronic Fatigue and <u>Immune Dysfunction</u> Syndrome.

Fear not, your immune system does work but the problem is that it is probably overworking and you know what happens to us when we overwork!

Dr Bell feels that, similar to ourselves becoming exhausted through overwork, the same thing could be happening to our immune systems. He describes the immune system in ME as

being in *"a state of chronic activation"* (always working).
> *"as a consequence, perhaps, some immunological functions are impaired, from the exhaustion of being chronically* (long term) *challenged."*   *(Disease of a Thousand Names. Bell)*

The suspect workings of the immune system may be due to it working so hard for so long.

Let's have a closer look at this workaholic immune system of ours. What does the immune system actually do? Why is it so important?

A Typical Working Day

The immune system is the body's way of defending itself against the unwanted micro-organisms such as bacteria, viruses and even fungi. These organisms can get into the body in a variety of ways, such as in food, through a cut in the skin, by breathing them in when someone sneezes and, most common of all, by handling food with hands that have picked up microbes. That's how you catch a cold, for example, hence the need to cover your mouth and nose with a hankie when you sneeze, and to wash your hands regularly. Once in the body the organisms multiply, start to do all sorts of damage and you have an infection. The body has been invaded and you become ill.

Left alone these invading organisms could run riot through the body, using the bloodstream for transport. It's a bit like a foreign army invading your territory. If there is no resistance, no defending forces waiting for them at the border, the invading troops could easily take over.

However, the invading micro-organisms in your body will meet with a very special defending force - the immune system.

This system, if it is working well, is able to defend the body by identifying the enemy, tracking it down and eliminating it. Like a good army, the immune system has specialised forces, effective transport, good communication and lethal weapons.

The immune system is complex but it might help to understand it if we think of a military analogy. Our immune system will become an army. Our specialised forces are the white blood cells, which use the blood stream for their effective transport. Communications are handled by the brain and central nervous system; the lethal weapons are chemical!

Our specialised forces are the white blood cells

Army Headquarters

The headquarters of this army is in the Bone Marrow, because this is where all the white cells are manufactured. Put simply, when they are made, the cells split off into different 'regiments', where they are educated into the different jobs that they have to do.

Some of the cells are designed to wake up the immune system and alert it to an enemy attack. Others make special proteins called antibodies which will latch onto the invading organism and immobilise it. In the same way as only one key will fit a specific lock, each antibody will be made to match a specific type of microbe.

Some cells are designed to attack and kill while others will tell the immune system when the battle is over. After the battle, yet more specialised cells clean up the debris.

The diagram opposite shows the white cells leaving the Bone Marrow Headquarters and becoming separate 'regiments'. Half of them become B Cells, Macrophages and Natural Killer Cells:

B Cells	- are the Design Team
Macrophages	- are the Heavy Mob
Natural Killer Cells	- are the S.A.S.

The other half head for the Thymus Gland, a small gland situated in the top of the chest, just behind the breast bone, to form the T-Regiment:

T-Helper Cells	- called Cytokine Kid
T-Suppressor Cells	- are 'All Clear' wardens
T-Killer Cells	- are the Ground Troops
T-Memory Cells	- work the Computer Data Base

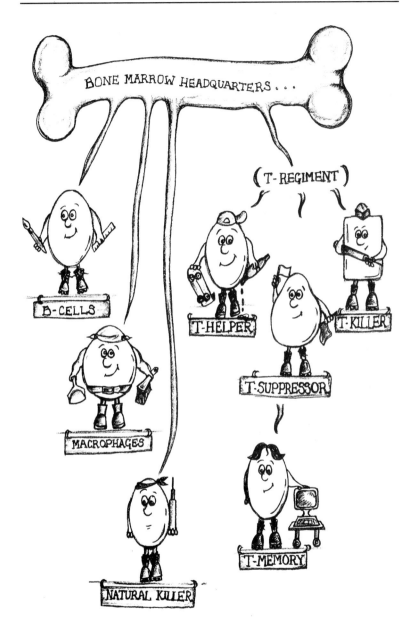

Half of the cells become three separate 'regiments'.
The other half form the 'T-Regiment'.

What do these cells do in the Immune System?

*   T-Memory Cells - *Computer Data Base*

Any previous encounters with enemy organisms, will have been entered in the data base of these T-Memory cells. Should

the need arise, a quick sort through the computer details will allow the immune system to jump immediately into action, with the right information to locate the enemy.

It is these cells that will store the information when you are given vaccinations.   These cells are alerted by the 'reveille' (wake up) signal, given by the T-Helper cells.

*   T-Helper Cells - *Cytokine Kid*

These are a fairly well-disciplined division of the army, although in the ME patient they may be getting a little over-zealous at times.

Once an invader, such as a virus, is recognised, the T-Helpers wake up the Immune System by producing chemical 'messages' called cytokines which are spread around the body in the bloodstream.

*   T-Killer - *Ground Troops*

Receiving the cytokine message from T-Helper, the Ground Troops leap into action, identify the invader from the chemical message and kill it. T-Killers find the cell that contains the offending organism and inject it with poison. The cell wall dissolves, causing the insides to spill out.

When the Ground Troops get the 'All-clear' message from the T-Suppressors they stop fighting and take a well-earned rest. The Macrophages are left to clean up the mess.

*   T-Suppressor Cells - *'All-clear' Wardens*

These cells sit ready with their 'flags' to give the 'all-clear' signal. It is their duty to inform the immune system that the battle is over and normal surveillance should now be the order of the day.

In some ME patients, however, these troops seem to spend too much time away from their post and the 'all-clear' signal is slow to be given.

*   B Cells - *Antibody Design Team*

These cells design antibodies for any new organisms that are found. Remember that an antibody is like a special key to fit a specific lock. If a virus, for example, is recognised as a previous invader, the B Cells can immediately call up the antibody template that was used before and manufacture many more antibodies.

These specially designed cells lock onto enemy organisms acting as a ball and chain to immobilise them. The offending microbe is held down until the Macrophages come along to clear up.

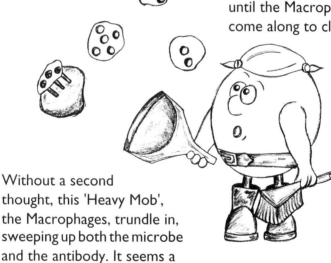

Without a second thought, this 'Heavy Mob', the Macrophages, trundle in, sweeping up both the microbe and the antibody. It seems a shame that the antibodies found themselves on a suicide mission. Still, I suppose the B Cells can always put in a bit of over-time and manufacture more antibodies.

*   Macrophages - *The Heavy Mob*

These are the largest cells in the immune system. They roam around the body eating up dead and dying tissue and devouring incapacitated foreign bodies such as viruses.

'All brawn and no brain' could be the unkind label for these cells as they are unable to recognise invaders on their own. William Collinge, in his book 'Recovery from ME', explains how a Macrophage will take a piece of material from the invader and bring this evidence to the attention of the T-Memory cell for identification.

*   Natural Killer Cells - *S.A.S. Troops*

These are specialised troops which, unlike the T-Killer Cells, which await messages from T- Helper and T-Suppressor to start or stop the action, are independent and free spirits. The Natural Killer Cells roam freely, always on the look-out for invading organisms and infected cells.

Viruses spend very little time circulating in body fluids. They must get into a cell quickly to replicate themselves and survive, so it is important for these S.A.S. troops to identify viruses and kill them quickly, using the same poison gun as T-Killer.

With good teamwork, the immune system
works harmoniously

Teamwork

With good teamwork, the immune system works harmoni-ously. The T-Memory cells search through their data base to see if they have any information on the invading micro-organism in front of them. The Natural Killer Cells, always on the look-out for enemies, may have already used its independ-ent system to recognise and kill off any attack. If this hasn't happened, then the T-Helper cells will sound the battle-cry with their cytokine guns and wake up the rest of the immune system.

The B Cells will be busy designing antibodies while the T-Killer cells will be fighting the cells containing the enemy with their chemical weapons. The Macrophages will be trundling around clearing up the mess and when the battle is won, the T-Suppressors will sound the all-clear and everything will return to normal.

What a very useful system. With a defence force like that you would think it would be impossible for any invader to gain a foothold. In fact, many contacts between microbes and the immune system end in a truce. There is a balance in which the microbe persists and the immune system keeps it in balance. For example, once you've had measles and chicken pox these viruses persist for life with no further symptoms. You are now said to be immune from measles/chicken pox. It is this balance between the microbe and the immune system which may be a problem with ME sufferers.

I started this chapter by explaining that perhaps our immune systems were trying to be too useful, or working too hard. Remember the phrase 'chronically challenged'? Let's take a look at why our systems may be working too hard or be out of balance.

The Immune System and ME

When you first contracted the virus, why didn't your immune system agree on a truce? Did the T-Helper Cells wake up the system? If they did, why didn't T-Suppressor sound the 'All-clear' when the battle was over so that you could return to school/college? Was there a battle at all or did the invading virus have a free hand? Is the virus still lurking in the cells?

These are difficult questions to answer. Studies from around the world have shown different results. William Collinge, writes about one study carried out on ME patients in America, following an outbreak near Lake Tahoe in 1985. These patients were found to have far more T-Helper cells than expected. In a normally balanced immune system T-Helpers outnumber T-Suppressors by about 18:10. In the Tahoe study the T-Helpers outnumbered the T-Suppressors by 32:10. However, in other parts of the world the opposite was found to be happening.

T-Helpers usually outnumber T- Suppressors by 18-10.
In the Lake Tahoe study they outnumbered them 32-10.

No wonder the research workers find it so difficult. Dr. Darrel Ho-Yen in his excellent book 'Better Recovery From Viral Illness' states that the symptoms of PVFS (ME) may be produced by two mechanisms:

1)"reduced ability of the immune system to deal with infection or

***2)** by the immune system becoming activated after an infection and unable to switch itself off."*   *(Ho-Yen)*

In terms of our immune army we might say that:

1)

Insufficient numbers of T-Helpers may fail to give the wake up 'reveille' signal loud enough, allowing the virus a free rein to invade cells and replicate.

or

2)

Insufficient numbers of T-Suppressors may fail to give the 'All-clear' signal loud enough.

The greater number of T-Helpers may then be having a fine old time with their cytokine guns.

Although the research teams have had different results as regards the activity of the T cells, more agreement has been found when Natural Killer cells have been studied. Collinge mentions one interesting study by Dr. Nancy Klimas, a leading immunologist from the University of Miami. She found higher numbers of Natural Killer cells in ME patients, as if the immune system was trying to respond to something and had sent out a lot more S.A.S. troops to find the infected cells. Just as it should be, I hear you say but the problem with all of these Natural Killer cells, was that they were not working efficiently. Collinge quotes:

> *"These cells seem to feel the way that patients do - they're exhausted."*   (Recovery from ME. Collinge)

Why ME?

Taking in all the above information, when the virus attacked your body, the model that I would like you to think about has just three points to it:

A) The T-Helpers were over-zealous with their cytokine guns.

B) The T-Suppressors were slow to give the 'All-clear'.

C) The Natural Killer Cells were, and possibly still are lethargic and lacking commitment.

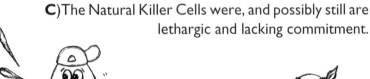

Even if you disagree with the model, it seems clear that whatever the fine details, the immune system is reacting in an abnormal way. How, then does this cause all the many symptoms of ME?

Dr. Jay Goldstein, Director of the Chronic Fatigue Institute in Beverly Hills, California writes that the illness is:
> "a virally induced, cytokine-mediated, psychoneuroimmunological disorder that occurs in genetically predisposed individuals."

Now you know why you feel so awful! It sounds horrendous doesn't it? William Collinge goes a long way in explaining Goldstein's description and I would recommend his book, 'Recovery from ME', if you wish for a fuller, more technical version.

My interpretation of Dr. Goldstein's description is:
> If your body is in a **susceptible state** when **a virus enters** the body, the **chemicals that are produced** may indirectly affect your **brain and central nervous system**, causing the illness known as ME.

Let's take a closer look at this interpretation.

*   "Susceptible State"

Not everybody who has a virus gets ME; far, far from it. However, at the time of the viral infection, the physical and mental state that your body is in, may play a part in whether you go on to get ME. Physical and mental stress can just tip the balance of the Microbe v Immune System that I wrote of earlier.

This word 'stress' may conjure up a picture of someone completely unable to cope but it is not like that. Many of life's events can cause stress and we fully believe that we can cope with them all, especially the pleasurable ones - falling in love, disco until the early hours, trudging through the night on a hiking expedition, are all perfectly safe in themselves and very enjoyable. Some events are less pleasurable - exams, interviews, breakup of relationships, parental divorce, death of a loved one, are again, perfectly safe in themselves even though they are painful to go through. All the above experiences, including the pleasurable ones, are stressful.

The Oxford English Dictionary gives 'stress' as meaning a demand on physical or mental energy. It does not mean that you cannot cope.

Dr Shepherd in his book 'Living with ME', states that excess physical or mental stress, at the time of the original viral infection can make you more susceptible to contracting ME. He describes an experiment, reported in the 'New England Journal of Medicine' in 1991, to see if people suffering from stress are more likely to succumb to illness. Four hundred healthy volunteers were given nasal drops. Some of the people had common cold viruses added to the drops whilst others received sterile drops. This way they didn't know if they were expected to catch the cold or not.

The stress levels of the volunteers were measured and it was found that those with the highest stress levels were far more likely to succumb to colds.

It is interesting that after the Royal Free Hospital outbreak, it was the medical staff that went on to suffer from ME, while only a handful of the patients did. The latter were, of course, already sick and you would think that it would have been those people that went on to contract ME, not the fit doctors and nurses. However, the medical staff were having demands made on their physical energy, whereas the patients were not.

*   "Virus Enters"

When a doctor suspects that a patient may be suffering from ME he or she will carry out a series of blood tests. These tests often come back indicating that the patient has had a virus, hence the label that is sometimes used: 'Post (after) Viral Fatigue'.

Earlier in this chapter we saw that as a consequence of our immune system responding to this virus the system may now be out of balance.

Some medical workers feel that an active virus is persistent in the body and they may say: "When the virus goes, then the ME symptoms will go."

Perhaps a better statement is the one used by Dr. Ho-Yen:
"..when the immune system returns to normal it is accompanied by the patient getting better".
                    (Better Recovery From Viral Illness. Ho-Yen)

We know that a normally functioning immune system will be immediately alerted when a microbe enters the body and that chemical messages are sent out to deal with it.

*   "Chemicals that are produced"

Remember our picture of the immune system being like a well-disciplined army, with different divisions all programmed to do different things? The problem with the army of an ME sufferer is that discipline in several of the divisions is not all it should be.

We know that the function of the T-Helper cells is to switch on the immune system when the body is under attack. They spray chemicals called **cytokines** into the bloodstream when the body is under attack from a micro-organism.   These chemicals are the messages that are received by the T-Killer cells to enable them to identify and destroy the virus.

It is these chemicals, and not the virus itself, that give you all the 'flu-like symptoms: swollen glands, headache, aches and pains in the muscles and joints and the complete lethargy. It is worth remembering that when you feel like you are "coming down with 'flu again", it may be that the cytokine gun has been at work. It may not mean that you have contracted another virus.

"Every few weeks I get a cold or the 'flu. I have a sore throat and my glands come up. The doctor gives me antibiotics and they seem to work until the next time."
(YP 17yrs)

Apart from making you feel very poorly, what other damage could the cytokines do? When you realise that these chemicals are in the blood stream it is an easy step to see how they can affect the delicate tuning of the brain and the central nervous system.

*   "Brain and Central Nervous System"

Dr. Shepherd explains in his "Guidelines For The Care of Patients", a booklet for General Practitioners, available from ME Head Office:

"..It has now been established that cytokines can be produced locally within the brain .... and from immune cells which enter via the circulation. Cytokine production can, in turn, produce changes in mood and cognitive function (knowing and understanding), appetite disturbance, fatigue, increased slow-wave sleep and even the destruction of neurons (nerve cells)."   *(Guidelines. Shepherd)*

Deep inside the brain is a small gland called the *Hypothalamus*. This gland controls many of the body functions - **temperature, sleep, mood, appetite**. Now think about the major symptoms that are found in ME: the difficulty with temperature control, sleep disturbance, mood swings and changes in appetite. It is easy to see why the Hypothalamus is thought to be affected in ME patients.

Could the cytokine chemicals be affecting this gland?

Cytokine Kid is in the dock charged with affecting the delicate tuning of the Hypothalamus.

The Hypothalamus, in its turn, produces its own set of cytokine chemicals, called Interleukins, which produces fatigue and other typical ME symptoms. This particular chemical is well known as a cancer fighter. What is interesting is that when cancer patients were given Interleukin, the patients all had very classic ME symptoms. When the course of Interleukin was stopped, the patients felt better.

This again points the finger of suspicion at the cytokine chemicals for the many and varied symptoms of ME - more evidence for the prosecution!

You can see, therefore, that:

> If your body is in a **susceptible state** when a virus
> enters the body, the **chemicals that are produced**
> may indirectly affect your **brain and central nervous
> system**, causing the illness known as ME.

The disturbances in the brain are explained more fully in Chapter 5 but for now, it might be helpful for you to remember that if you put any demands on your body while you are feeling unwell, then your immune system may react.

Excess physical or mental activity may have your T-helper cells leaping into action with their cytokine guns, leaving you feeling dreadful.

If the T-Suppressors are not responding to what is happening, then Cytokine Kid can reign supreme!

5

The Brain and Central Nervous System

"My brain just stopped working. I was so frightened."
(YP 13yrs)

We have seen in the last chapter, that cytokine chemicals could be the cause of all the 'flu-like feelings we get: sore throat and neck, aching limbs, headaches, etc. These symptoms, debilitating though they may be, are ones that we understand. They are familiar to us.

When you've had 'flu in the past, you spent a few days in bed or on the settee, perhaps being pampered by mum or dad. You felt awful but were able to watch television or read a magazine. Your concerned friends rang you up or dropped by to keep you up with all the news. After a week or so you were back to normal. You got better and your friends understood.

It is a very different matter when your brain seems to stop working. This is not familiar, it has never happened before. You feel ill but you cannot watch television - you find it difficult to follow what the programme is about, it's all going too fast. You cannot read a magazine - the words run into each other or you forget what the previous paragraph was all about. It is embarrassing if your friends visit. They talk to you. They are waiting for you to reply to something they have just asked and you've forgotten the question! So you tell your friends not to call because they seem to talk too loudly anyway. But then you are lonely.

"I told people not to come round, that I would phone them. I just wanted to sleep, be quiet, any noise made me feel nervous. But then, when nobody came I got very down in the dumps."   (YP 16yrs)

It is all so frightening. Are you going mad? You have no previous experience to draw on. What is going on?

Am I Going Mad?

"What is really peculiar is when I try and go for a walk. Firstly I can't walk and talk at the same time. Secondly, when I come home I find that when I try to say something I say the wrong word."   (YP 14yrs)

No, you are not going mad (demented). Dr Shepherd tells us that:

"Whichever parts of the brain are involved in M.E., there certainly does not seem to be any dementing process.

.....patients (or their friends) may notice that they are using inappropriate or opposite words without realising it (e.g. saying 'hot' when they mean 'cold'), or are completely unable to remember a familiar word or name - what doctors call anomia.

Rest then restores the energy levels and relatively normal function returns."   (Living With ME. Shepherd)

This could have something to do with the lack of blood flow to the brain. In the last few years doctors have found that, by using sophisticated machinery, coloured pictures of the brain called SPECT scans can be taken.

The resulting pictures (a bit like coloured X-rays) indicate changes in the blood flow to certain parts of the brain. In some ME patients an abnormally low blood flow has been seen. This happens with some other neurological illnessses so it is not a diagnostic test for ME, merely another pointer as to what may be going on. If you lie on your arm awkwardly and restrict its blood flow, your hand quickly becomes useless so it is an easy step to see why some of the brain functions become useless if its blood flow is restricted.

The energy level required by the brain is quite remarkable. Your brain is only 2% of your entire body weight but it consumes 20% of the available energy. With the brain needing so much of the body's available energy, it is easy to see that *any* over-exertion, mental *or* physical, will have a direct toll on our brain functioning. Read too long or climb the stairs and you could be calling your brother "Rover"!

Knowing how much energy the brain needs may explain why we often say the wrong thing but is that the reason for losing concentration? What is happening when you start a sentence and then forget what you're talking about? Why is the brain only able to do one thing at a time, when normally it has been capable of taking on a variety of tasks simultaneously?

When I was fit, and teaching in a large comprehensive school, I would be walking down a corridor at the end of a lesson, weighed down with books, when invariably a student whom I had taught a few days before, would jump out in front of me.

"What was that homework, Miss?"

Under normal circumstances, it would not have been difficult for my brain to cope with all the information that it was receiving at that single moment. Sensory signals would be received as students bumped their bags into my shins. My ears would take in the corridor noise as well as the student's question. My eyes would monitor the growing crush outside Room 22 and the brain would be deciding whether the class should be let in early. Parts of the brain that controlled balance would be fighting to keep hold of the books in my arms. In spite of my brain having plenty to keep it occupied, it was still able to recognise the student and search the memory banks for the information that was required - Jane Smith\Homework\Class 9GH\Tuesday Period 4.

"It was page thirty six, questions two and four. And it must be in by Friday," I would reply, still with one eye on Room 22.

My brain had no problem with the multiplicity of tasks.

Then I became ill with ME and could no longer cope with more than one brain function at a time. Messages given to me over the phone for my husband, were immediately forgotten. If he was really lucky I may have remembered the caller's name! This is the frightening part. This is when you think you're going mad. Surely this is more than the brain running out of energy.

Does it mean that part of the brain that deals with short term memory is damaged? This could account for people with ME getting lost in the middle of spoken sentences. As soon as the information is received by the brain, it seems that it is forgotten.

Perhaps a more comforting thought might be: 'not forgotten, just misunderstood'. When the information is received by one brain cell, perhaps it is passed on incorrectly to the next brain cell and finishes up giving the wrong message altogether.

Have you ever played Chinese Whispers, a game where one person whispers a message into your ear and you have to pass it on to the next person? By the time the message has passed through about ten people it is distorted, if more transfers are made the whole message becomes completely garbled.

So are the brain messages becoming garbled or distorted in people with ME? What does this wonderful machine called the brain do anyway?

The Brain Machine

Let's take a closer look at how the brain works. Everything we see, hear, feel, touch or smell registers in our consciousness and our brain determines how we should respond to each stimulus. As we gaze upon a beautiful scene, the brain may simply commit the scene to memory - no action is required. If you listen to your favourite pop group your brain may insist you get up and dance - well, if you have enough energy!

All this processing of information and use of memory requires millions of tiny brain cells called *neurons* to communicate with one another. Under the microscope, we are able to see exactly how each neuron is able to pass on information.

Neurons Under The Microscope

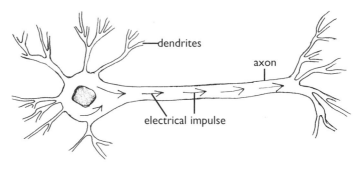

DIAGRAM OF NEURON

Simplified, the main body of the neuron has tree-like branches called *dendrites* coming out of one end and a long thread like structure called the *axon*, coming out of the other.

The dendrites receive the messages from the other cells. These messages, in the form of *electrical impulses*, pass from the dendrites, through the main body of the cell, to the axon.

The axon must now pass the message on to the dendrites of other neurons - but there is a problem. The axon is not in direct contact with other dendrites. They are not touching. There is a microscopic gap between each neuron, known as the *synapse* which has to be overcome.

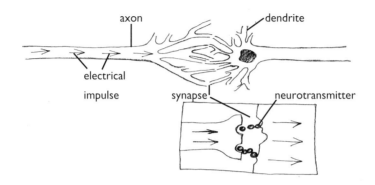

DIAGRAM OF TWO NEURONS SHOWING THE
ELECTRICAL ENERGY CROSSING THE SYNAPSE

Crossing the Synapse

How does the message manage to cross the synapse and find another dendrite? Small though this synapse is, the electrical impulse that is carried through the cell and down the axon cannot jump the gap to get to another dendrite.

In order to cross the synapse, the electrical message has to change to a chemical one. Special chemicals called *neurotransmitters* are waiting at the end of the axon to cross the synapse; rather like a ferry boat waiting to cross a river. When the electrical message arrives, it pushes the neurotransmitters out into the synapse. The electrical energy has now changed into chemical energy.

Like the ferry boat sailing across the river to its own jetty, the neurotransmitters are looking for their own homes or *receptors*. When the correct receptor is found on a dendrite, the neurotransmitters stimulate it and the chemical message returns to an electrical one.

That's how it should happen but what might happen with the ME patient? Is your 'boat' leaving the 'jetty' with the right message? Is it able to land at its jetty on the other side of the synapse?

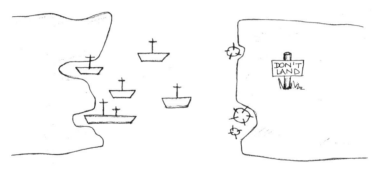

Are your 'ferry boats' able to land at the jetty on the other side of the synapse?

Medical evidence tells us that chemicals and viruses can interfere with the brain function, blocking the receptors. It's as if our ferry boat is being shown a 'Don't Land' notice when it arrives at its jetty on the other side of the synapse. The neurotransmitters are unable to lock into the dendrite and pass on the message. Doctors working with ME patients have found that this happens in the Hypothalamus:

> "Receptors in the hypothalamus are then switched off leading to disturbances of appetite, sleep, mood and temperature regulation"   (Children With ME. Dr Alan Franklin)

If these hypothalamic receptors in the ME patient are becoming blocked, are there any drugs that cancel out this effect? Some patients show improvement when prescribed anti-depressants (an awful name when you're trying to prove to people that you are not depressed). However, the chemicals in these tablets can act as extra ferry boats.

More ferry boats (neurotransmitters) mean that there is more chance of them finding a receptor that it can lock into and pass on the message.

Pollution?

What chemical could be causing this damage in the synapse? Remember the chemical cytokines that our helpful little T-cells spray out when a virus is spotted? Perhaps these cytokines could interact with the receptors in some way and block them.

Is this further evidence in the C.K. Trial?
In C.Ks defence they are not the only organism capable of doing this. Viruses can also lock into neurons and cause damage.

If the neurotransmitters are unable to pass on their information correctly then, surely a situation of Chinese Whispers could easily occur. The messages could become distorted or they may lose their way in the synapse altogether. We only have to think of the brain's reactions to the chemical alcohol. If alcohol can disrupt the brain workings of a healthy person, it is easy to see what disruption the cytokine chemicals may be capable of, if you suffer from ME.

Next time you go to walk through a doorway and you suddenly find yourself up against the door pillar, don't worry! Take one step to the left (or right) and try again. When you get lost in a conversation, tell your friends that your neurotransmitters seem to have missed the ferry boat - that will get them thinking. On second thoughts that will probably convince them that you have gone mad and we know that definitely is not the case!

*   *   *

Cytokines and the Hypothalamus

Not only may the cytokine chemicals be arranging games of Chinese Whispers amongst the neurotransmitters but, as we saw in the last chapter, they may also be acting on that very important gland in the brain, *the Hypothalamus*. This gland is tiny, only the size of a pea, and sits deep inside the brain but despite its size it is the master controller of many important functions. It governs:

*	**Temperature control**
*	**Appetite**
*	**Mood**
*	**Sleep rhythm**

If the cytokine chemicals are some-how affecting the Hypothalamus, which governs the above four functions, Cytokine Kid has a lot to answer for as we suffer from poor temperature control, disturbance of appetite, mood swings and insomnia!

Let us look a little closer at how the disturbance of the Hypothalamus may be creating such problems for us.

*   Temperature Control

Many patients with ME have great difficulty with temperature control. Most of us have continual cold feet and hands and are wrapped up in winter woollies while others are into their tee shirt and shorts.

*   Appetite

The loss of one's appetite causes many problems. We understand that we must eat to 'keep our strength up' but it is all so exhausting. You may feel hungry before you eat and your family has carefully prepared your favourite dish. Two or three mouthfuls and you feel full. You also feel very guilty for the time and energy it took to prepare.

A good balanced diet is essential to assist the workings of our body. 'Little and often' is the most helpful regime if appetite is a problem for you.

*   Mood Swings

The silliest things will make us burst into tears. Our moods are unpredictable.

"Worry and tears over the smallest things are a problem but his aggressiveness was hard for all the family to understand and cope with."   *(Carer of 16yr old))*

"I find it hardest of all to cope with her mood swings. I never really know how she'll feel on any given day, and, since I don't know if the illness is responsible for her mood, I find it very difficult not to patronise her unintentionally."   *(Carer of 17yr old)*

It is important to realise that the problem lies within this very small gland, the hypothalamus, and is therefore, not within the patient's control. It is easy for everyone, including the patient to make fun of the problem with the body's thermostat - you can turn up the heating while everyone else strips off. It is much more difficult to deal with mood swings.

Panic attacks, especially amongst young people with ME, are very common. The heart rate and release of adrenalin when we are frightened are part of the *autonomic nervous system*, which is also under the control of the hypothalamus. If the hypothalamus is not functioning correctly it can speed up the heart rate and flood the system with adrenalin for no reason. Hence the feelings of panic!

> *"It sounds so silly but I get panicky if I am in the same room with a lot of people."*   (YP 14yrs)

> *"I have lost all my confidence. I seem to panic at the smallest thing. I feel humiliated, very tearful. I never used to be like this."*   (YP 17yrs)

It is understandable to feel humiliated when you are experiencing embarrassing emotions which are completely new to you. Take comfort from the fact that they are common feelings in fellow ME sufferers.

Children under the age of eleven have mood swings that can take on dramatic fluctuations from utter fatigue to hyper-activity.

> *"His emotional lability and difficult behaviour when he gets 'high' make any family outings hard going."*
> (Carer of 10yr old)

"It doesn't take much to reduce him to tears or, alternatively make him fly off the handle. One minute he's flaked out, lying on the settee, next minute he's chasing the cat round the room. It's very difficult."
(Carer of 9yr old)

As the sufferer gets older they understand that they must rest physically but they complain of their brains being switched on all the time:

"My brain is sometimes on super-fast mode. I can't seem to switch it off."   *(YP 14yrs)*

*   Sleep Rhythm

The difficulty with sleep causes such concern that I have devoted the whole of the next chapter to it. At this stage, though, it is important to understand that it is probably the malfunctioning of the hypothalamus which is causing the disturbance of your sleeping patterns. Dr Richard Ferber, director of a centre for sleep disorders in children, which is attached to Harvard Medical School explains the importance of having a normally functioning hypothalamus:

"To develop a normal sleep-wake rhythm one must have a normally functioning hypothalamic pacemaker with normal input."
(Sleep Schedule-Dependent Causes of Insomnia and Sleepiness. Ferber)

If we cannot sleep, it is no wonder that we have such overwhelming fatigue.

"If only I could sleep for a week, maybe I would feel better. I just lay awake and use up more energy than ever."   *(YP 19yrs)*

Does the lack of sleep really consume our meagre supplies of energy? We desperately need to restore our energy levels and surely the best way of doing that is to cut our brain activity to a minimum and sleep.

But sleeping is so difficult!

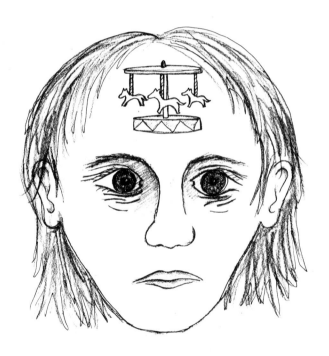

"The inside of my head just goes round and round."
(YP 18yrs)

6

Sleep Problems

Insomnia

Soon after birth, we are taught that it is normal to be awake during the day and to sleep at night. This is considered so important that the first time a baby sleeps right through the night, all the family get to hear of it and there is a general celebration.

When we are no longer babies and illness disturbs our sleep pattern, we become concerned that we are behaving abnormally. We worry about the effect that this may be having on the family.

"My child's problems were greatly exacerbated by guilt at not going to sleep. She saw the problems that it creates for everyone else."   *(Carer of 13yr old)*

Why should we feel guilty about not sleeping?

Perhaps we can all remember our parents saying to us: "You get a good night's sleep and you'll feel better in the morning". With ME, we wake in the morning not feeling better, in fact very often, worse than we did before we went to sleep. We then feel guilty for not getting the good night's sleep that our memories have told us was so beneficial. The carer above recognised this problem in her child and took time to reassure her that there was nothing wrong in being unable to sleep.

"We stressed the need for rest and encouraged her to use the time for daydreaming and making up pleasant little stories." **(Carer of 12yr old)**

We also might take comfort from Professor Jim Horne who is director of the Sleep Research Laboratory at Loughborough University. In his book 'Why Do We Sleep', he suggests that while deep sleep is necessary to rest the brain, sleep is not essential for most bodily repair processes. This, he states, can take place just as well during periods of 'relaxed wakefulness'. Dr Ho-Yen agrees with this:

"With PVFS (ME), sleep is disturbed, variable (4-16 hours) and vivid dreams are common. These are all normal findings and should not be a source of worry. I am happy if patients are in bed for 10 hours with their eyes closed, and not listening to the radio or music. I do not worry about how often they wake or their vivid dreams."

(Better Recovery From Viral Illnesses. Ho-Yen)

Stages of Sleep

While the two doctors above are saying that 'relaxed wake-fulness', for most bodily repair processes, is satisfactory, it is the brain that needs the rest in ME patients. Professor Horne points out that in order to rest the brain, really deep sleep is needed. This deep sleep is often called 'Slow Wave Sleep' because of the patterns that are made when the brainwaves are measured on an electro-encephalogram (ECG).

Sleep is measured in four stages:

* Stage One - the lightest stage. It is that lovely drowsy feeling when you are just aware of what is going on around you. The heart rate drops and our muscles relax - relaxed wakefulness.

* Stage Two - a mixture of light sleep and deeper, unconscious sleep. This stage occupies about 45% of our sleep and is the stage that Professor Horne feels is 'optional sleep'.

* Stage Three - a stage that occupies only about 7% of sleep and in it the brainwaves are slowing rapidly.

* Stage Four - Slow Wave Sleep. The deepest form of sleep, and the most essential.

Professor Horne has found that when subjects were deprived of sleep by staying up all night, they did not need to catch up with all the lost sleep. They only needed to recover the deepest form of sleep, together with some of the stage one. Professor Horne suggests, therefore, that only this Slow Wave Sleep is really essential, the remainder is *"optional sleep...filling the tedious hours of darkness until sunrise"*.

But with ME, even getting into the first stage of sleep seems impossible.

"When I try to go to sleep my brain seems to be whirring around all the time. It's like a merry-go-round in my head."   *(YP 16yrs)*

This lack of sleep could be adding to our symptoms. Several research projects have indicated the essential nature of Slow Wave Sleep in patients with ME. Even with healthy subjects, muscle pain is increased when Slow Wave Sleep is disturbed:

"These subjects displayed increased joint tenderness during the three nights of Stage Four sleep deprivation...they complained of musculoskeletal aching, stiffness, generalised heaviness and unusual somatic (body) fatigue....

All these symptoms subsided over the subsequent two nights of undisturbed sleep."

(Fibromyalgia, Sleep Disorder and CFS. Moldofsky)

This study was on healthy subjects who, on being able to recover their lost, deep sleep, found that their symptoms went away. If only it was that easy for the ME patient!

Tracking Down The Culprit

We've seen in the last chapter how it is possible for the neurotransmitters to have their receptors blocked by cytokine chemicals; remember the ferry boat being unable to land?

Things are hotting up for C.K!

When specific cytokines have been administered to healthy subjects there has been a disturbance of the sleep-wake cycle.

One of the forty or so possible neurotransmitters is one called *serotonin* or *5HT* which controls many functions, including sleep. In the hypothalamus there are many receptors for this transmitter to lock into. If the cytokine chemicals could be interfering in the synapse, then they could be preventing the important 'now go to sleep' message from getting through.

In the previous chapter you read about extra 'ferry boats' being given in the form of anti-depressant tablets. These may contain serotonin, which is why the sleep problems are often eased with anti-depressants. However, these tablets are not without their side effects and doctors may be reluctant to give them to young people.

There is little that we can do if the hypothalamus is malfunctioning. It is beyond our control. We shouldn't feel guilty, therefore, about not getting enough sleep. We should take the carer's advice at the start of this chapter and 'daydream', until our brain will allow us to get into the valuable Stage Four sleep.

What about getting the Stage Four sleep during the day?

Change of Sleep Cycle

"I toss and turn all night, completely unable to sleep. Then when four or five in the morning comes round I go off and don't wake up until about two or three in the afternoon."   *(YP 16yrs)*

If you are in the severe, toxic stage of ME (see Chapter 11) or your body is needing to sleep fourteen or sixteen hours a day, it is better for you to sleep on. Similarly, one or two short sleeps during the day can be very beneficial. My concern is for the young person who is not able to sleep at night but sleeps heavily throughout the day.

> *"I don't really get too fed up during the day because I'm usually asleep. It's at night that I get bored. I read then or watch television."*   *(YP 18yrs)*

It has been said that the change of sleep cycle in patients with ME is particularly acute in the younger age range i.e. under twenty years. Personally I do not think that the younger person is affected any worse than an adult. It is just that the younger person has more opportunity to allow their sleep rhythm to shift. With an adult suffering from ME, there is invariably action in the household early in the morning. The adult may remain in bed but he or she is drawn in to what is going on downstairs.

"Where did you say my sport's kit was?"

"Can I bring this form up to you, Dad, my teacher said it has to be in today".

A quieter start to the day would have been appreciated, I'm sure, but the point is that adults are generally woken at the start of the day. The parent of a young sufferer allows the younger person to sleep on.

Richard Ferber, director of a centre for childhood sleep disorders, who explained in the previous chapter that one must have a *"normally functioning hypothalamic pacemaker"*, goes on to suggest that if <u>some</u> function remains, provision should be made for:

> *"strong, regular, daily cues, including daytime bright light and night-time darkness."*   *(Ferber)*

Those of you who are not waking until the very late morning or early afternoon should begin to have the curtains pulled back earlier and earlier, in order to prevent a change in sleep cycle. Nothing drastic, perhaps ten or fifteen minutes earlier every three or four days. Ideally you should continue to do this until you are in tune with the family and being woken with them. Rest should continue in bed once the light has been let in as most people with ME take a long time to get themselves together at the start of the day.

Often you feel at your worst in the morning, not refreshed by sleep and feeling sure that another hour or two would just set you up nicely. Unfortunately, it rarely does. This is worth remembering if you are managing to go to school/college at all or, indeed, if you have home tutors to visit. Your brain needs at least an hour and a half to get up to speed.

A Moving Cycle

I hear stories of young people whose sleep rhythm gently pushes round, so that one month they are sleeping at night and a couple of months later, find themselves sleeping during the day:

> *"His sleep pattern has become a cycle, sometimes sleeping all day and awake all night, then gradually moving round to night sleep and so on."*
>
> *(Carer of 16yr old)*

There have been many studies of healthy volunteers being completely shut off from outside light or stimulation of any sort. Not knowing when one day ends and another begins, they have chosen when to go to bed and when to rise. Interestingly the subjects' body clocks invariably took up a twenty-five hour rhythm instead of the expected twenty-four hour.

If this is the natural order of things, without the sunlight cues, it could account for a slow change of sleep cycle that young people find themselves getting into if they are allowed to choose their own sleep-wake times.

It is for all the above reasons that I suggest young sufferers should keep in with the family cycle of events as much as possible. However, I will reiterate that if severely ill and needing to sleep long hours, then this should be encouraged.

This brings us on to the vexed question, "How long should I stay in bed if I'm not sleeping?"

Of course, everyone is different and only the patient really knows how he or she is feeling. Too much activity will leave the patient feeling worse, too little, once the severe stage has passed, may cause the muscles to waste. It is this careful balancing act that is explained in the next chapter.

7

Muscles and Exercise

*"Exercise-induced muscular fatigue is the cardinal feature of
ME."*   *(Living with ME. Shepherd)*

In other words, if you have ME, any physical effort will cause
the muscles to become very tired indeed. Fatigue is the chief
symptom of the illness. A diagnosis of ME will not be made
unless abnormal fatigue is present.

The big question is:

Where is that fatigue coming from?

View 1 - The problem is in the muscles

The muscles themselves are damaged, they tire easily and then
become painful.

View 2 - The problem is in the brain

The brain is sending the wrong messages to the muscles and
causing them pain. Painful muscles are then rested, they lose
bulk (get smaller), tire easily and become more painful when
used.

Before we look at some of the evidence for these two views,
let me explain how muscles produce energy. It might be a clue
as to why we have so little of it!

First, think of a car. Petrol is the fuel and this is stored in the
tank, waiting to be used. To make the car move, the petrol is
called to the engine where it is burned and energy is produced.

The food that you eat is your fuel, in particular the carbohydrates. Take breakfast, for example, it may consist of cornflakes sprinkled with sugar. Both the corn and the sugar are carbohydrates. When these carbohydrates are digested, they are broken down and stored in the body as a chemical called glycogen. Like the petrol in the car which waits to be called to the engine, the glycogen waits to be called to the muscles.

Inside every muscle cell are mitochondria, little factories which make energy. These factories call up the glycogen and mix it with their own self-produced enzymes. They also need oxygen which they take from the red blood cells. These chemicals all react together to produce energy.

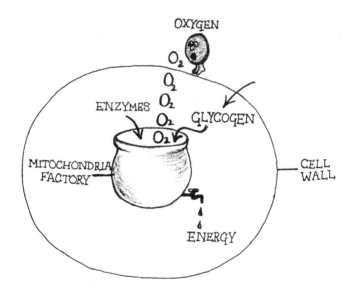

Inside every muscle cell are mitochondria,
little factories which make energy.

Returning to the two arguments:

1) Damaged muscles

If the mitochondria 'pot' is damaged, or if some of the chemicals that are needed are missing, then it is clear that energy will not be produced.

2) Brain sending incorrect messages

The brain sends messages through the central nervous system to the muscles. If the message does not get through (remember the ferry boats that couldn't land), then the glycogen may not even be called, and again, energy will not be produced.

Those that believe in the first argument may say that the muscles are damaged, so you should not exercise them.

Those that believe the second argument may say that there is nothing wrong with the muscles and you should exercise. Too much rest will cause damage to the muscles.

Many doctors nowadays are of the opinion that neither long term total rest, nor excessive exercise is the best way to get better. Although scientists have found that both the above arguments have substance, there is a danger in believing one argument and denying the other.

It is not a clear-cut case of Exercise or Don't Exercise. Both sides have valid points. Both sides must be listened to.

Let us look at some evidence which suggests that both sides may be right.

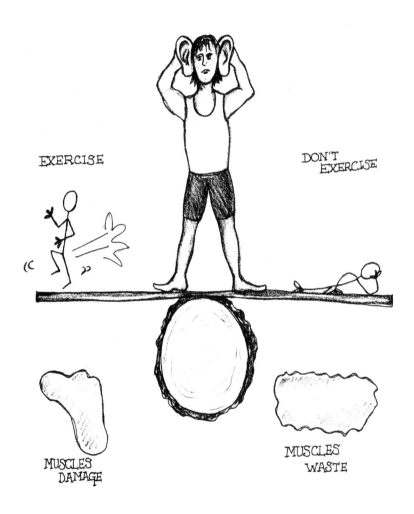

EXERCISE

DON'T
EXERCISE

MUSCLES
DAMAGE

MUSCLES
WASTE

Both sides must be listened to.

View 1. The muscles are damaged - Don't Exercise.

In 1991 Dr Wilhelmina Behan, working at the department of Pathology at the Western Infirmary, Glasgow, published a paper called 'Mitochondrial abnormalities in the Postviral Fatigue Syndrome'.

We know that mitochondria are the little energy producing factories in the cell. The muscles, needing a lot of energy, are rich in mitochondria. In a simplified form you can think of the mitochondria as an egg-like structure, filled with carefully folded cristae.

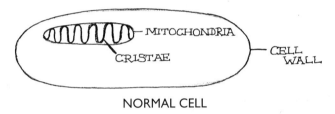

NORMAL CELL

Dr Behan's team examined pieces of muscle that had been taken from 50 patients who had ME. In 40 cases they noticed startling differences in the mitochondria of the patients, compared to healthy people. Instead of the usual long, convoluted, folding pattern, the mitochondria had swollen. There were separate compartments, round vacuoles and some splitting open of the outer membrane.

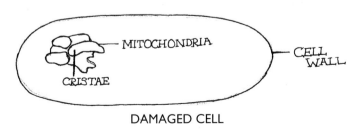

DAMAGED CELL

The changes in the mitochondria were only found in muscle samples of the patients, never in the connecting tissue.

If the muscle cell is damaged, surely exercise would be harmful? The pain that one experiences, in the leg muscles particularly, makes it very difficult to try any exercise anyway. Even after significant bed rest, the muscles can feel as if they have run a marathon.

What can cause the muscle pain?

We have seen how energy is made in the mitochondria from oxygen and enzymes. If oxygen is not present then instead of energy coming out of the mitochondria pot it is lactic acid. In modern terms we call it 'going for the burn'. The burn being the pain of excess lactic acid.

Dr Russell Lane, together with a group of researchers, has been looking at whether ME patients have an abnormal level of lactic acid in their muscles following exercise. Reporting in the Journal of Neurology, Neurosurgery and Psychiatry in 1994, they showed that in some ME patients the production of lactic acid in their muscles happened more rapidly than was normal.

Ten years earlier, Dr. Charles Shepherd was involved in a similar research project with similar results. Dr Shepherd, discussing this study writes:

> "All normal human beings produce lactic acid during exercise but the results here showed a rapid and excessive acidity in the muscle, indicating a clear abnormality in the way the mitochondria were breaking down glycogen."
>
> (Living With ME. Shepherd)

If the muscle cells are damaged as the above studies have indicated, then resting up and not using those muscles might seem the best idea. After all, if you break a bone in your leg it is immobilised until it is mended. The difference is that a broken bone can be mended in a matter of weeks. The damage to muscle in ME patients may be on-going, with no known time limit to its impairment.

Dr Len Archard, a molecular virologist at Charing Cross Hospital Medical School is working on a theory that a damaging virus may be persisting in the body, continually changing its structure to fool the 'B' Cell design team in the immune system.

Working on a similar theory, F.McGarry, part of the Behan team, reported in 1994 that they had found particles of a type of virus known as enterovirus in the muscle, heart and brain of a deceased patient with ME. This virus normally attacks the intestines. With the virus remaining in other parts of the patient's body it would indicate an on-going infection, supporting the 'persistent virus' theory that Dr Archard is working on.

So, unlike the broken leg, to give a time-limit for recovery is impossible.

If virus particles are present in the muscles for a long time then surely rest is best.

Dr Ho-Yen points out:

".. when a battery is run down, one does not make it better by using it, but rather by allowing it to recharge."

(Better Recovery From Viral Illness. Ho-Yen)

However, Dr David Smith in his book 'Understanding ME' states:

"Do too little for too long and the muscles disappear." (Smith)

Ah! Perhaps it is time to look at the second argument.

View 2. Wasted muscles need building up - Exercise!

In his book, Dr Smith mentions the time he has spent with Professor Richard Edwards who is the head of the Muscle Research Centre at Liverpool University. These meetings changed the doctor's view of muscle damage in patients with ME. He now feels that a biochemical change has happened in the muscle, due to 'low, habitual activity' (doing very little for a long time).

In order to try to understand his viewpoint, let us return to a healthy muscle.

Muscle is made up of fibres. These fibres can increase in mass to produce the huge biceps of a weightlifter, or decrease in mass to produce a thin looking leg such as when a plaster cast is removed.

Each muscle fibre is filled with mitochondria. We know that these mitochondria break down glycogen and produce energy. The more energy that is required, the more mitochondria 'factories' will be needed.

A weightlifter, for example, may just be able to lift 100Kg. He does not have the available energy to lift 120Kg. The mitochondria in his arms have given their all.

With careful and regular training, this weightlifter may increase the mass of muscle fibre and consequently increase the number of energy-giving mitochondria.

More mitochondria factories - more energy, so that eventually he may be capable of lifting his 120Kg. This may take many months of regular practice, slowly asking the muscles for a little more.

More mitochondria factories - more energy

Dr Smith explains that if you do not exercise sufficiently (i.e take too much rest) then you can lose mitochondria:

> *"Becoming fit is a slow process, you have to really work at it. Getting unfit, on the other hand, is rapid and is much easier......one is going to get biochemical and structural changes occurring that can be very difficult to reverse."*
>
> *(Understanding ME. Smith)*

Dr Smith goes on to explain that the process of reducing the mitochondria takes 'only a few days'.

But what do we do? When you have ME, even the thought of taking a bath can seem impossibly tiring, never mind building up muscle tissue!

Thankfully Dr Smith does not recommend weight training as a cure for ME, neither does he suggest a high level of exercise. Disappointingly though, he does feel that the advice - Stop Before You Get Tired - is 'unreasonable', suggesting that if everybody lived by that rule, they would gradually finish work earlier each day. This slothful behaviour, he suggests, would increase the tiredness, culminating in a *"permanently, irrevocably bed-bound"* position.

It is my experience that young people who are in the Convalescent Stage of ME (see Chapter 11) do not stop *before* they get tired.

They don't even stop when they *are* tired, very often.

> *"I didn't help myself as I was determined to pretend there was nothing wrong with me."*   *(YP 19yrs)*

It is usually after the event that one looks back on the danger of exercising.

"I was told to exercise at the start of my illness and I am convinced that is why I became severely ill. I tried so hard to keep up with my friends but I just couldn't."

(YP 16yrs)

The weightlifter, before training, knew that 100Kg was the point to stop. He would have done a lot of damage in lifting 120Kg or even 110Kg, before he was ready. Similarly, you must find your limit. To exceed that limit will exhaust your muscles.

"My consultant told me to take at least an hour of hard physical exercise every day. I followed the exercise programme for a few weeks. I was, at first, physically sick and very soon became unable to do anything other than the one hour of exercise. Finally, I was unable to do even that and needed many weeks in bed to get over it. I returned to the doctor unable to walk at all."

(YP 20yrs)

It is my opinion that to listen to one argument only can lead to problems:

Exercise - and you exhaust the muscles which may be damaged in the first place anyway.

Don't exercise - and you lose some of the energy giving mitochondria.

The word 'exercise' is perhaps too reminiscent of long cross-country runs. I prefer to use the word 'activity'. **The amount of activity for each of you will vary.** Like the weightlifter, you have to find your limit.

Those of you who are in the severe (Toxic) stage of ME - see Chapter 11 - will need a great deal of rest, especially if there is any evidence of an active viral infection.

> *"ME not only responds to rest, it <u>demands</u> it."*
>
> *(Carer of 14yr old)*

We have seen that viruses can remain in muscle cells and we want to give our immune systems the best chance of catching the enemy and destroying it before it goes to ground. By resting, both physically and mentally, we allow the body's own healing mechanisms the best chance.

But how do we know if it's too much resting or too much exercise? Perhaps we need a little walking-man symbol inside our heads, like the flashing man on the Pelican Crossing Lights.

If any of you ever saw the film 'Rainman', Dustin Hoffman, who played a mentally handicapped man, was walking across a wide and busy road in America. When he was halfway across, the 'Walk' sign changed to 'Don't Walk'. He stopped still, right in the middle of the road, not caring about the car horns protesting and the people staring at him. The rest of the people who had been crossing ran on but he stood his ground, staring at the 'Don't Walk' sign.

If we were able to stop when the 'Don't Exercise' warning light came on: if we could ignore those around us that give us funny looks when we have to leave the party early, then we would avoid exhausting the muscles, whilst being careful not to allow them to waste.

Section Three

Through

the

Forest

8

The Forest of Emotions

"When I first became ill, it was as if I had been very suddenly abandoned in the middle of a dense forest. I seemed to be shouting for help and no-one was hearing me. I felt very alone and isolated. I didn't know which way to turn.

The undergrowth was thick and it was a struggle to make progress.

As I came to terms with my illness, I found it easier to fight through the undergrowth. I began to see other people's paths and tracks.

I started to progress on my journey and I finally saw an opening - and daylight. I'm keeping my sights set on the daylight and I think I am on the right path."

(Julia 19yrs)

Julia found herself in the dense forest of emotional turmoil that everyone feels when they realise that they have such a debilitating illness. She felt unable to cope: *"suddenly abandoned in the middle of a dense forest"*. She was shouting for help but: *"nobody was hearing me"*. Her parents and boy-friend would quickly say that of course they could hear her and they had responded to her needs at every turn. However, press them further and they may agree that at times, they have felt exactly the same - just as lost, just as unable to cope and just as alone. Everyone has to come to terms with ME, not just the sufferer. Everyone will go through a forest of emotions.

This 'forest' is laying at the foot of the ME mountain that we want to climb. Unfortunately there is no way up the mountain without first going through this forest but as we follow the paths and tracks of others, we will look at the 'trees' that represent our emotions and you will realise that they are all the normal feelings that everyone experiences. When, like Julia, you find the daylight I can guarantee that you will have learnt a lot about life in general but more importantly a great deal about yourself.

The Real Me

"Everybody misses the real 'me' - especially me!"

(YP 13yrs)

Those of you who have had a slow onset of ME have probably been searching for the old 'you' for some considerable time. Those who were perfectly well one week and then very ill the next, maybe feel like Julia - suddenly abandoned in the middle of a dense forest. This feeling is not linked with how poorly you feel, nor does it depend on the length of time you have been ill. It is all about understanding the feelings that you are having and accepting the illness:

"I don't want to think about being so ill. I can't seem to get my head around all that is happening."

(YP 13yrs)

I can understand how this young person is feeling. He might feel better in the short term to sit looking at the mountain and stay out of the forest but as I mentioned in the introduction, if you stay where you are, staring at the mountain you will feel useless and inadequate. You will also be missing the 'real me'.

If you stay where you are, staring at the mountain you will feel useless
and inadequate. You will also be missing the 'real me'.

We can't turn the clock back. We have to accept what has
happened and learn from it. All of life's experiences change us
in some way, there are always new paths that have to be found
and old ones left behind.
Does this happen to everyone?

Servicemen and women may return from war completely unscathed physically but it is likely that the terrible experiences they suffered will have changed them in some way. Much as they may wish to rejoin the path that they were on before the war, it is often impossible. The more it is agonized over, the more confused they will become. These are men and women who had been prepared for war; they knew what to expect but they may still find it very difficult coming to terms with the emotional feelings of treading a new path. How much more difficult it would be for them if they were not prepared.

Were you prepared for a long-term illness before it happened? Were you or your family even told what to expect at the time of your diagnosis? Unless you were very fortunate the answer will be no.

"Our doctor was extremely supportive and listened but he didn't seem to know much about ME".

(Carer of 13 yr old)

It is no wonder that you feel lost, frightened and frustrated, spending your last remnants of energy trying to find the old 'you'. Before you had ME, things came easy. Physically the old 'you' could manage anything, now it is a struggle. Don't worry, the old 'you' has not gone away, it merely needs a new road to travel down. This road may take longer for you to reach your destination but when you do arrive you will be a calmer, wiser, more knowledgable, mature, young person.

At the moment you may be in turmoil, not knowing which way to turn; whether to laugh or cry, stay quiet or shout out aloud. These emotional feelings are all perfectly natural and are part of any feelings of loss or enforced change.

Loss and Change

Everyone who has had change forced upon them or has lost something precious in life will have been through a very similar forest to the one growing at the foot of your mountain. In order to try to prove this, why not try the following exercise, perhaps with a friend or a parent?

Forget about ME for a moment. I want you and your mum/dad/partner to think of a situation when you lost something precious - sentimental or monetary - or were forced to make a change in your life. For example you may have lost a gift that your best friend gave to you - you may have had a very expensive CD player stolen - or it may have been a loved pet that died.

Alternatively you may have been forced to make a significant change in your life - you may have had to move house and hence lost your friends. How did you feel about this situation?

Writing it down is best but talking about it can be nearly as good. Even laying down and thinking about it can be useful.

Exercise 1

Think about when you lost something precious or were forced to make a significant change in your life.

* What happened directly after you had lost that precious item or was forced to make that life change?
* How did you feel about yourself and towards other people?

         *   *   *

When you have completed this exercise, read my story, about the time when I lost something precious.

MY STORY:

Shock	I parked the car in the carpark overlooking the lake. The dog jumped out, eager for his walk. Realising that my new handbag (a birthday present from my husband) was on the front seat, I pushed it out of sight in the foot well and locked the doors.
	Half an hour later I returned to find the front door window smashed and my new handbag missing. I felt sick, vulnerable and lonely. No one was around. Putting the dog in the back, I drove the half a mile or so back to my home. It was almost as if I could put the clock back. The sun was
Denial	shining, my dog had enjoyed his walk and I would give him his dinner when I got in. All was well. If I blinked my eyes my handbag would be back on the seat and the window intact. It wasn't like that.
Anger	As I drove up to the house. I suddenly felt very angry indeed. So angry in fact, that on blurting out my story to my teenage son, he thought that I had been actually threatened by the thief.
Return	I insisted that we return to the lake - but wasn't sure why. I was so churned up and angry that my son didn't even ask. On arriving, I leapt out and began frantically searching for my bag in the undergrowth. We searched for a long time until I began to feel overwhelmingly guilty.
Guilty	I really should have put my bag in the boot. I've made my son late for meeting his friends, they'll think I'm mad dragging him out. What would my husband say? He'll think I didn't treasure the bag. I could have had a cheap one off the market but no, I wanted an expensive one.

Shock

When we arrived home, I sat on the settee until my husband came home. I was numb, in shock I suppose. It was really quite a small incident but it had built up in my mind to something astronomical.

       *   *   *

The words down the side of the story show the five emotions that one goes through at the time of loss/change.

These are the five 'trees' that we need to find, identify, acknowledge and pass:

> **D**enial
> **R**eturn to how it was
> **A**nger
> **G**uilt
> **S**hock

Go back to <u>your</u> story.

Can you put **D - R - A - G - S** to any part of your story in the way that I have with my story? The order is unimportant.

Talk the story through with someone, until you feel comfortable that what you experienced were very natural emotions.

These, then are the five most common feelings that you get when you are involved with loss or change. There are others, especially the need to be very busy, but they are not as troublesome as DRAGS.

DRAGS and ME

The second and third exercises concern your illness. Again it is very useful to do this with someone close to you. You won't be climbing this mountain alone. Your mum, dad or partner will be with you and it is just as scary for them. The more you can discuss how you feel about ME, the easier it will be to cope with day to day living:

> *"My daughter doesn't speak much about how she's feeling, she doesn't want me to get upset. But I need to know in order to help her. I suppose it helps her to know how I'm feeling as well."*   *(Carer of 14yr old)*

Exercise 2

This activity again concerns the five emotions: denial, return, anger, guilt, shock. Look at the five quotes below - some from young people and some from their carers. The sentences are lettered A - E. Decide which sentence goes with which emotion. In the table opposite, fill in the letter against the most appropriate emotion.

> *A   "I know it really is ME but I sometimes think that perhaps I haven't looked after her properly." (Carer)*
> *B   "I get so angry when my friends phone up and tell me about their boyfriends."   (YP)*
> *C   "He doesn't read any of the ME magazines. He doesn't seem to want to know"   (Carer)*
> *D   "All my friends are taking and passing exams. I want to be there with them. I imagine walking into the exam room with them."   (YP)*
> *E   "I heard mum talking on the telephone last night about how ill I was. Hearing it from somebody else hit me really hard"   (YP)*

Emotion	Letter
Denial	𝑎 C
Return	d
Anger	B
Guilt	A
Shock	E

How did you get on?

My suggestions are below but don't worry if your answers disagree with mine or your carer come to that. It really doesn't matter whether you agree with each other or not. I'm sure that you thought through your reasons for deciding that a particular statement goes with a particular emotion, and that is the important part.

You may have disagreed with the named emotions that I placed on my story about losing my handbag. That doesn't make either of us right, it just means that we see things slightly differently.

This is just an exercise to get you to realise that many of the emotions that are troubling you at the moment are perfectly natural.

My suggestion
for Exercise 2:

Emotion	Letter
Denial	C
Return	D
Anger	B
Guilt	A
Shock	E

Exercise 3

Now, a similar exercise but this time see if you can write some sentences about your ME to fit in with the emotions.

As before, it is more fun if you can do this with someone who is close to you. You both need to get a plain sheet of paper, separate it into five wide lines and copy the headings below.

DRAGS	Sentences about my ME
Denial	
Return to how it was	
Anger	
Guilt	
Shock	

Using these DRAGS headings, write a sentence or two about your ME. Be as honest as you can.

Below are some pointers to help you but it would be better if you could write in your own thoughts without having suggestions put in front of you. The pointers are written in the present tense but you may choose to write in the past tense:

* Write about times when you refuse to learn about the illness, hoping that it might be something else?   **Denial.**

* What happens when you try to return to how you were before the illness?   **Return.**

* What makes you really angry?   **Anger.**

* What makes you feel guilty?   **Guilt.**

* What are the full implications of having ME?   **Shock.**

How did you get on?

If you wrote things down, did you write in the present tense:

"*I get very angry when*..........", as if it was happening now.

Or did you write in the past tense:

"*I got very angry when*..........", writing about something that happened before?

Did you find it easy to identify your feelings and slot them into the right space? If you did, then you probably also wrote, or spoke, in the past tense.

This would indicate that you are probably through that part of the forest now and, like Julia, can see a bit of daylight.

If you wrote in the present tense, especially if you also had problems in finding something to write, then you are probably still lost in the forest, unable or unwilling to see the 'trees'.

This is perfectly natural. You are not the only one to be feeling like this. It is all part of the illness. Other young sufferers feel exactly as you do.

Other People's Forests

Exercise 4

In the next exercise we share an extract from Annabel's diary. The whole diary covers a time period of one year.

In the same way as I identified the DRAGS emotions in my story about the stolen handbag, see if you can do the same with this extract. Use the box at the side to jot down the most appropriate initial letter of DRAGS, as I did with my story.

Extract from Annabel's Diary. Aged 15 years.

September

"After eleven months I have finally been diagnosed as having ME. It took a long time before people, even my own family believed me. I had lots of blood tests taken - even on my 15th birthday!

Happy Birthday Annabel.

When they all came back showing normal I began to wonder what was really the matter with me. It coincided with a character in a serial I was watching on television actually dying from Leukaemia. For a while I was really frightened as I felt a lot like she was feeling.

November

I have not been to school since the beginning of October and missed out on a half term trip to Paris and EuroDisney. The week they were away I kept wondering what they were doing and the fun I was missing. I just wanted to be with them.

February

My leg joints and muscles are even worse, I'm in agony, I feel so old and I'm all bent over. Every night I go to bed and tell myself this is all a dream and I will wake up in the morning and be fine. My brother has been so good since I've been ill and so has dad. I don't know what I'd do without mum. All our lives seem to be totally messed up because of ME.

March

Woke up this morning and can't move my right hand. My left is stiff but not as bad as my right. My fingers won't move. What's happening to me?

I'm so frightened but at the same time angry. What more do I have to put up with?

May

Dad has been ill and I am blaming myself. He is worried about me as well as other things at work. Oh how I hate myself.

Had to go to see the specialist again. I never want to see him again! He just didn't understand and I don't think he wanted to either. I feel very angry. He told me that I was nearly sixteen and didn't look very attractive in a wheelchair! I resent his intrusion. Mum and I had set a pace which I was coping with, taking each day as it came along and then he upset everything. I hate him.

June

Woke up this morning and thought I'd lost control of my bladder - whatever next! Thank heavens I soon discovered that my hot water bottle had burst.

I went to sports' day in my wheelchair - it was horrid. I should have been running with the others. I hate life. Have been very poorly this week. I'm hot but feeling very cold. I started shaking so badly I couldn't even hold a drink. My legs wouldn't keep still and I keep going terribly dizzy. I feel dreadful and very frightened. What is happening to me?

September

I'm trying to go back to school for half a day a week. It felt strange putting on my uniform again. It is hard to explain how I felt - a mixture of feelings really. I was worried, anxious, nervous, fed up at the thought of how far behind I was and frustrated.

October

Have this awful throat bug that keeps coming back. Am trying to go back to school for a couple of hours a week again. If only I can manage it I might begin to feel normal again, like everybody else.....please.....

I hope that by sharing in Annabel's experience you are able to see some of the same 'trees' - Denial, Return, Anger, Guilt, Shock - in your forest. They are the natural and normal emotions that everyone goes through that has lost something precious. It is called grief or the mourning process; letting go of the old pathway and finding the new one.

The only danger in this forest trek is if you refuse to acknowledge any of the emotional trees - perhaps deciding all that is written in this chapter is twaddle.

You are, of course, welcome to your opinion but I can guarantee that if you continue to return to your old life, without first accepting that you are ill, you will make yourself worse.

Acknowledge each 'tree' in turn and you will have accepted your present limitations and will be able to work towards a recovery.

The following chapter will take the grief process one step at a time. Looking at each emotional tree in turn, we will share the experiences of others and will learn how to pass on through the forest and out into the daylight.

9

DRAGS

"The most important point in looking after an ME sufferer is to recognise your anger, fear, denial and despair as part of normal coping mechanisms.
Accept that you will both go through a grief process."
(Carer of 15yr old)

This is good advice but as a race of people, we are not very good at grieving. News pictures from the Middle East show local mourners shouting and screaming; something that Westerners have difficulty with, although it is a very healthy way to mourn. If you yelled out of the window the neighbours would think you abnormal and yet it would simply be your way of coping and actually very therapeutic.

Perhaps you don't have the energy to shout but we don't even discuss our feelings very well, do we? When friends come round, it is very difficult to tell them how ill you feel.

"If only she would trust people enough to tell them how she's feeling but she uses up all her spare energy putting on a mask for people, pretending that she's OK."   *(Carer of 12yr old)*

Let's not forget, though, that all this grieving and coping is not just down to the ME sufferer. Everyone close to them will go through a grief process - mum, dad, partner, brothers and sisters. All will feel denial, anger and guilt.

"To see my son so ill and not be able to do anything for him is very hard. Having to cry inside and keep my feelings to myself wears me down but I have to keep strong for him."   *(Carer of 18yr old)*

The carer above is very hard on herself. The bottom line is that she loves her son and is doing everything that she can, physically, allowing him to rest and making him comfortable.

To assist him emotionally, both for his sake and her own, she needs to go into the DRAGS forest with him. She is denying her own feelings (crying inside), watching him wandering around the forest whilst she looks on, feeling useless.

If you can face the emotions of loss together, it is much easier. Letting each other know that there is every good reason to feel the way you do, allows the journey through the forest to continue.

We know the names of the emotional 'trees' that we'll see in this forest, so let's take a closer look at each of them.

Denial

"My dad doesn't read, or take any interest in the ME information. He is just all bubbly and bright with me, telling me I'll be fine in a week or two." (YP 15yrs)

This may seem harsh but this denial of the true side of things is very common, especially amongst members of the family who are not directly involved with the care of the patient.

"To defend ourselves against the hurt of unacceptable news, the mind either fails to comprehend or tries to accept preferred, alternative information."

(Why I Am Afraid To Grieve. Carpenter and Johnson)

Denial is one of the first emotions that you have to deal with in any form of loss and a difficult one to face up to. It's far more comfortable to pretend that you will be fine next week than to accept that ME is long term illness that needs working at.

"I thought that if we talked about her illness she would really worry about the future. So we talked about the past as if she wasn't sick at all." *(Carer of 12yr old)*

The carer above is trying hard to maintain an illusion in order to keep her daughter positive but by doing this they will both be in denial.

Maintaining illusions wastes vital energy. Don't turn away from what is in front of you. Learn about the illness and you won't have to 'talk about the past'. The future is not as bleak as it may appear. It only seems so when you don't fully understand the illness.

About ten years ago, my husband and I were fortunate enough to have a holiday in Malaysia. Part of this holiday took us down a river with jungle on either side. My understanding of what a 'jungle' would be like, made it look black and impenetrable from the boat.

In fact, when we explored the jungle, there were very few ground plants at all. Much of the light was unable to get through the canopy of trees, so nothing small grew. A far cry from having to hack our way through with a machete that you see on the films!

Without the knowledge, I had imagined something quite different. Learn about your illness and it will not seem as bad as you think.

Don't assume that others won't understand. Give them a chance. By explaining about ME yourself, the illness will become more real to you and far easier to cope with.

"ME has such a bad name in some circles that I'm afraid to confess that I've got it. When people ask questions about my illness, I panic and say it's like glandular fever because everyone knows about that."

(YP 21yrs)

If you've read this far in the book, then I would suggest that you are not denying your illness and you are doing everything you can to understand. What may be happening, however, is a denial of the 'chronic' (long term) label. The shock of reading about the average length of the illness often drives carers and patients to look for the quick cure.

"Mum spends all her spare time tearing around looking for alternative therapies that she thinks will have a magic effect."   *(YP 17yrs)*

I often find that young people with ME are far more realistic about bogus claims of cures than adults.

"Yes we've been there, tried that. It's just another to tick off the list."   *(YP 15yrs)*

Return

The immediate family, who may be desperate for things to return to normal, may put you under pressure to 'do a little more', as soon as some improvement is seen in your health.

This is to be encouraged but only a <u>little</u> more. It is sometimes too easy to be saying, 'perhaps you can go back to school next month'.

The reality is sometimes difficult to take in.

Return is closely aligned to denial and can often be difficult to see as a separate emotion. However, if you deny the implications of ME and try to return to an old lifestyle before you are completely better, then you are likely to relapse.

> *"My family are suggesting that as ME stopped me from going to University, I should try an Open University course. I don't really want to start with the O.U. because I'm looking forward to the sport and social life at University."*   *(YP 20yrs)*

The family above recognised their daughter's urgent pleas to 'Return' and offered an alternative.

This young woman may not be able to hit the 100% better for some considerable time and it is rather foolish to be thinking of restarting her academic career in such active terms. Rather than desperately trying to 'return to how it was' - or 'might have been' - she should be thinking of an alternative way to achieve a degree; always providing, of course, that she really feels able to study.

By turning back to the Ability Scale in Chapter 3 you will see that some home study can be achieved when you are about 60-70% able. It will take a good few years for this young woman to be able to take on the stimulation of University life and the academic study and the sporting opportunities and the social life. I think that the Open University course is well worth thinking about.

When we first become ill, many of our waking hours are filled with thinking about what our friends are doing.

Exam times are especially difficult if you have done much of the course work and preparation towards GCSE or 'A' levels. The frustration of not being able to prove yourself is overwhelming. This is very much part of 'letting go of the old pathway' and it can cause a lot of sadness.

> *"I cried when I saw the TV news about others getting*
> *their results and hugging one another. I think it upset*
> *mum as well because she ran out of the room."*
> *(YP 16yrs)*

What an ideal opportunity for both the young person above and her mother to recognise their frustration and sadness together. They could have hugged and cried as one rather than both suffer in isolation.

Discussing how you feel and why, is the healthy way to identify the emotional 'trees' and acknowledge them. Once acknowledged, you can pass on to the next one.

The feeling of needing to return is an emotion which may arise on many more occasions but you will recognise it more quickly the next time and be able to deal with it in an appropriate way.

> *"I feel a failure when people I know have attained*
> *heights that I wanted for myself. I should have been*
> *there."*   *(YP 19yrs)*

Go slowly up the ME mountain - don't be tempted to run back out of the forest to your old lifestyle.

Anger

One emotion that you will definitely recognise quickly, both in yourself and others, is anger.

When people shout at each other or become abusive it is easy to recognise their anger. What is more difficult to spot is displaced anger. With this, you become convinced that it is all the other person's fault. *You* are not angry, it's just the others being horrid. Note the displaced anger in the extract overleaf from Eve's diary as she complains about her uncaring friends.

"......I don't belong any more. I look different, I act different, I have ME. Does anybody care? I work just as hard as my friends but do they understand what it's like to be alone? I don't think they want to know what it's like. They don't understand the tests, the pain, the tiredness. Nobody understands and lots will never understand or even try to understand."   *(Eve 13yrs)*

At the time of writing her diary, Eve did not recognise how angry she was. It was only when she looked back to the time of her diagnosis that she realised how differently she felt about things now.

"I can't believe how much I've changed since then."
                                          (Eve 14yrs)

This indicates how very useful a diary can be.

Carers also fall into displaced anger without realising it. There is always someone who will stand out as the whipping boy; someone who has said a misplaced word about ME. Maybe the doctor has given the impression of disbelief, maybe the neighbours or, more dangerously, maybe one of the family.

"I get so angry at his older brother. He just doesn't understand."   *(Carer of 15yr old)*

If other members of the family don't understand, then help them to. Sit them down, apologise for getting so angry and try to explain why. Give them a chance to have their say; allow them to show their anger and disappointment.

Although anger is a very normal emotion it can be a very frightening one. In general terms, anger is only destructive when it is allowed to build up to boiling point. However, even simmering point can be very frightening for you when you are also feeling very poorly and incredibly vulnerable. The age of adolescence in particular, is a time of great confusion and angry outbursts. Add a chronic illness to the emotions of growing up and it can become unbearable. The previously safe environment of home appears unsound when people around you are angry.

The situation is made worse for you, the teenager, if it is yourself who is angry. Irrational fears race to the surface:

"Sometimes mum really patronizes me. Just because I'm ill she thinks I'm stupid and it makes me really angry. I daren't say anything though because she might stop looking after me."   **(YP 13yrs)**

Anger makes us feel unsafe but we know that it will happen as part of 'loss' so how can we make it easier to bear?

Writing a diary is an excellent way to get rid of anger but you may not be able to cope with seeing your angry words written down. To have a permanent record of how you feel is sometimes difficult, especially if the anger is against someone close to you.

One really safe way to get rid of anger is to 'cast it to the wind'. Next time you feel angry, take a blanket or a rug and lay it on the bed. In the privacy of your own room, tell that rug all your angry thoughts. When you have no more left to say, roll up the rug very tightly, take it to the window and shake all those angry words into the wind.

This will save you from having to apologise to someone for your outburst and be left feeling guilty. There will be plenty of other things to feel guilty about without adding any more.

Guilt

This 'tree' is unavoidable. The others can be tiptoed past with a mere nod of acknowledgement but GUILT stands and blocks the way of anyone who has suffered a loss.

"If only I had ...." is so often heard. Even when there is absolutely no reason to feel guilty, the grieving person will find one. In order to ease this guilt, carers of young people often listen to every helpful titbit that comes their way.

"I've tried everything - alternative treatments, diets. Everyone seems to have heard of some weird remedy or another and you feel that you have to try it. I'd feel that I wasn't trying hard enough otherwise. The trouble is that the more treatments we try, the more hopeless it seems. I'm then left feeling guilty for raising her hopes."   *(Carer of 20yr old)*

This circle of guilt - action - guilt over the action - more action etc, does not help you through the forest. You go round and round the guilt 'tree', with each circuit looking bleaker and more frightening than the one before. It's rather like Winnie the Pooh and Piglet going round and round a tree in the snow looking for a Woozle. When they had been round once they came upon their own snowy footprints.

"The Tracks!" said Pooh. "A third animal has joined the other two!"

"Pooh!" cried Piglet. "Do you think it is another Woozle?"

Instead of using up vital energy walking round and round, recognise your inevitable guilt feelings for what they are - just emotional trees in the forest.

Occasionally guilt will hide behind the other three emotions, denial, return and anger, and in some cases become difficult to spot. Everyone can recognise the guilty feelings following an angry outburst. A quick apology can always make things OK again and the guilt melts away.

It isn't so easy when guilt follows denial, especially if someone has already pointed out the need for you to rest and not to deny the illness.

" I know my lifestyle played a significant role in why I feel so ill now. I was determined to live University life to the full regardless of what dad was saying. Consequently I took on far too much and frequently pushed myself to the limits of exhaustion. I now feel so guilty that they have to do everything for me."

(YP 21yrs)

By far the easiest way to deal with guilt is to share it with someone else. If you find it too difficult to share it with the person closest to you, then write to a fellow sufferer or carer who understands (The ME Association has contact names). Use a postal counselling service or have a counsellor visit you (see Useful Addresses).

Whatever else you do, don't try and hide your guilt or you will be left like Winnie the Pooh, walking round and round a tree looking for a Woozle, feeling increasingly guilty about feeling guilty.

Shock

Depending on your knowledge and experience of ME, shock will strike at any time. It may be the first emotion that you encounter, it may be the last.

More often than not it is the enormity of coming to terms with the expected length of the illness that is shocking.

A year out of a young person's life seems interminable, any longer is unthinkable. Who can really tell us WHEN? It is this uncertain time limit that is often the most difficult to bear.

"I don't let him read any of the ME material, it would
be such a shock for him to realise how ill he really is."
                                                    (Carer of 11yr old)

The carer's comments are correct, it will be a shock. What does he know already? What has he made a guess at?

He has probably filled in any blanks with the worst possible scenario. Far better to be honest with yourself and others and you can then continue out of the forest, fully trusting one another.

For most young people, shock comes as the last tree to be identified. The denial and the guilt are mostly behind them. I hope this is you. If it is then perhaps you can now spot a shaft of daylight coming through the forest.

If you are still struggling, then the next chapter will give you some pointers to help you see the daylight and find the right tracks out of the forest.

10

Daylight

To see the daylight through the forest is to accept ME for what it is - a long term, fluctuating illness. You have good days and bad days; times when you think it's all over and times when you think it never will be. It is not life threatening but it is life limiting - at least in the short term.

By accepting these limitations we are able to look forward, not back. Seeing the daylight is not tied to how you feel physically, you can be anywhere on the Ability Scale - Chapter 3 - rising or falling. Neither is it dependent on how long you have been ill.

"I've been ill now for over five years. I am a lot better and can do a lot of what I want to do but I find it very hard to be grateful for this. There is so much that I want to do and can't, and so much I have missed, and I am fed up with missing out."   *(YP 21yrs)*

If you spend time yearning over your lifestyle before ME then you are still looking back - 'Return'. You will not be able to climb the mountain successfully if your concentration is taken up with looking back at the old road. That's the quickest way to make a slip on the mountain before we've even started the climb!

"I know if I looked after myself and rested I would get a lot better but I can't help trying to do all the things I want to do."   *(YP 21yrs)*

This person can almost see the daylight but is finding it difficult to accept fully the limitations of ME and step onto the recovery road. This is the road of acceptance which leads out of the forest and into the daylight.

The illustration below shows a pathway through trees. Add your experiences to the drawing. Maybe you have many pathways to follow or maybe there are many more trees in the forest or scattered all over the hills. Draw in pencil and date the drawing. You may be surprised how much it will have changed in two or three months' time.

Acceptance

It isn't always easy to know whether you have really accepted ME and cleared the forest. If you are still in denial you could kid yourself of anything. If you can spot acceptance in others you can probably spot it in yourself.

Let's try another exercise.

Exercise

Take a look at the following quotes. Which ones do you think are from people who have accepted ME?

"I gave up worrying about what others thought about me and concentrated on using my energy to think of myself for a change; work on getting well." *(YP 17yrs)*

"She can't go out because she won't use a wheelchair. It's probably because people round here don't understand." *(Carer of 13 year old)*

"My ambition? That's a laugh. I've had to bring in the goalposts a hundred times closer." *(YP 20yrs)*

"The wheelchair is great. It means I can do all my own Christmas shopping. Mum is great, pushing me everywhere, we have great fun." *(YP 16yrs)*

"Life before used to be one big rush to achieve various things. Now I find that failure in some things isn't always the worst that can happen." *(YP 21yrs)*

"If I do nothing - which my doctor keeps telling me to do - for any length of time, I become depressed and demotivated." *(YP 18yrs)*

"I accept that I have ME but it's very hard not to feel that you are losing your active years." *(YP 14yrs)*

How many have really accepted their illness and why?

My conclusion is that four people are through the forest and three are not but you may not agree with me. Ask your mum/dad/carer what they think. Talk about why you think that someone has or has not accepted their illness. By talking through other people's stories you may find it easier to see where you stand.

It is important to realise that merely being able to recognise all the DRAGS emotions in yourself doesn't stop them from happening.

> *"All these angry thoughts and guilty feelings make me so depressed."*   *(YP 19yrs)*

It is natural to feel depressed, angry and frustrated. The whole family has every right to feel all of these emotions and many more. Accepting that they are there is the key. Not just for the sufferer but for everyone to acknowledge.

The most helpful support when you feel low comes from family and friends acknowledging how you feel.

> *"I asked my boyfriend to make sure he enquired about <u>my</u> day when he returned from work. Not just 'how did you feel (physically) today' but 'how did you cope with it today'."*   *(YP 23yrs)*

It is an opportunity to be reassured that it is OK to feel angry and frustrated. It had been part of her day and she wanted to share it with her boyfriend as much as she wanted to share in the happenings of his day.

If sharing your feelings does not come easy to you it may be helpful to talk or write to someone who can reassure you. Counselling has been mentioned in the previous chapter and addresses can be obtained from your doctor or Yellow Pages.

Failing that try the following exercise. It may help you to work through how you are feeling.

This chart is filled out at the end of each day.

Divide a page into 5 lines and head them:

DAY	
Situation	
Thoughts	
Feelings(DRAGS)	
So What?	

E.G.

1) Note the day and explain the 'Situation':
   Watching TV. Saw girls getting GCSE results

2) Your 'Thoughts' might be:
   I should have been there with them

3) Your 'Feelings' might be:
   Jealousy - RETURN

4) Under 'So What' you need to either assure yourself of the normality of your feelings:
   Of course I feel jealous when I have done so much of the work.

or look at the situation in another way:
   They worked at their lessons. I'm working on getting better. I can always get academic qualifications later.

Before you try a similar exercise yourself, take a look at the following chart by Rachel, a young friend of mine. The first few lines have been filled in exactly as Rachel had written them. The last few have been left for you to fill in your ideas.

DAY	Monday
Situation	Went swimming with other ME sufferers.
Thoughts	Great to be with others who are going through the same as me.
Feelings(DRAGS)	HAPPY!
So What?	------
DAY	Tuesday
Situation	Home with the family.
Thoughts	I feel really awful. I thought I was getting better. It's not fair!!
Feelings(DRAGS)	ANGRY
So What?	There is nothing I can do if my health is going down. I will rest.

DAY	Wednesday
Situation	Mum has been to the doctors. Doctor says back to work.
Thoughts	I don't want her to go. I want her to stay with me.
Feelings(DRAGS)	?
So What?	?
DAY	Saturday
Situation	At home at the weekend.
Thoughts	I wish mum would stop mothering me, she's driving me up the wall.
Feelings(DRAGS)	?
So What?	?
DAY	Monday
Situation	At home on my own.
Thoughts	I feel awful again, thought I was through all this. I overdid it yesterday.
Feelings-DRAGS	?
So What?	?

Try doing your own chart for a week or two. Very soon you will be mentally filling in the last line before you've even written the first.

How did you get on with Rachel's last entry? On Monday, she felt poorly again although she recognised that she had probably done too much on the Sunday.

When you have a 'bad' day, or even worse, if you have a severe relapse, it is very difficult to deal with. Just as you thought you were through the worst of it you are thrown back again.

You may well assume that you have fallen right back down the mountain and have disappeared into the forest.

> *"I think we're back in the forest. She's had a serious relapse and we're devastated."*   *(Carer of 17yr old)*

Back in the forest - or devastated over the relapse?

It is easy to confuse the sadness of becoming ill again with the DRAGS emotions. Before you assume that you've fallen into the forest again, answer this question:

Are you sad and confused because you want to be:

* 1) the person you were before you had ME?

* 2) the person you were before your relapse?

If the answer is the second one of these then you are already through the forest.

It is natural to feel sad and angry when you were doing so well.

If there is a reason for the relapse e.g. overdoing it, then you may also feel very guilty.

However, we all overdo it from time to time and if we can learn to listen to our bodies a little more because of it, then we have learnt a valuable lesson.

Don't give yourself a hard time over it!

You will see in the next section of the book that we relate relapses to slips and falls down the mountain. You may have slipped back into a little copse of trees but once through the main DRAGS forest you will rarely have to go back to the seemingly impenetrable part.

Knowing what the trees are, and realising that they are perfectly normal, will allow you to rest and accept the bad times as inevitable.

Two years after Annabel wrote her diary, extracts of which are in Chapter 8, she had a serious relapse. Although she was in a lot of pain and had fallen right down the ability scale to 0%, she remained optimistic.

Realising the reason for her relapse, there was no anger from having done too much, just acceptance that it was the wrong thing to have done. There was no desperate frustration just a better plan for the future.

"I'll come through this. I'll just take one day at a time. This illness is not going to go away overnight, I know that. Everything out there will just have to wait for me. That said, it still makes me very angry having to be bathed and fed!"   *(Annabel 17yrs)*

The various trees from the forest will be scattered along your route and you and your carer may bump into them at intervals.

Having been through the forest, you will recognise them instantly. Whilst Annabel felt rightly angry about the indignity of having to be bathed and fed, she does accept the limitations that ME brings: instead of looking back she is looking forward.

We now need to look forward to our route over the mountain.

Climbing the Mountain

11

Mountaineers

Picture the Mountain

The picture of the mountain and forest in this book is symbolic. It is meant as a representation of how your recovery path from ME might look to you. However, as we have already established, everyone is different and therefore everyone's mountain and forest will be different. The trees that make up your DRAGS forest might be thinly scattered around the mountain, all the way to the top; or they might be packed together at the foot of the mountain, never to be seen again once you are through the forest. Your mountain may be exceptionally steep with many peaks and valleys; or it may be fairly easy to climb and relatively smooth.

You were encouraged to add to the drawings in Chapter 10. You could also use the blank pages at the back of the book to draw your mountain and forest. Date your drawing and indicate where you think you are; in the forest, half way up the mountain?

In a few months time the shape of the mountain will have changed. As you climb you may encounter unexpected valleys that you couldn't see before; or you may find a short cut to a higher peak. Keep a record; note your ability level and add a few words. I would hope that your doctor shows an interest in such a record. Certainly a counsellor will be able to share your experiences, using the analogy of a mountain climb.

Three Types of Mountaineer

There are three stages of ME. Dr Alan Franklin (Paediatrician and ME Specialist) in his booklet 'Children with ME', describes them as:

* Stage One   - Toxic (Severe)
* Stage Two   - Convalescent
* Stage Three   - Recovery

Although there are no clear cut divides between each stage it will help us to understand the three stages if we think of them as representing three mountaineers:

* Toxic Tom
* Convalescent Carina
* Recovery Ricky

Tom, generally speaking, will spend much of his time in bed, a little time sitting in a chair and maybe the odd occasion out in a wheelchair.

Carina may be spending a lot of the time resting in a chair, with trips out in a wheelchair. At first walking is very difficult but gradually she will be able to walk further and further. She may be building up her studying from home and eventually be able to spend a little time in school.

Ricky will be having a regular rest period but be spending most of the time building up his physical and mental strength.

Tom

On the Young People's Ability Scale (Chapter 3 and Appendix) Tom will generally be less than 30% able. He may be feeling ill nearly all of the time and be constantly exhausted, even after waking from a long sleep. He may only feel comfortable lying flat in bed, being in constant pain all over his body. The weight of the bed quilt may be too much to bear and his skin can be hypersensitive to touch. Ordinary daylight is often too bright and he usually wants the blinds drawn. The radio, even on a very low volume, is too loud. He's beginning to understand why his parents were continually yelling upstairs, when he was well, to turn his music down. How did he ever stand it that loud anyway?

In some cases, total paralysis has been seen, whilst severe shaking episodes, inability to speak or swallow and periods of hyperventilation (very rapid breathing) are not uncommon.

Physical, mental and emotional rest is essential at this time. Talking and thinking drain Tom's small amounts of energy, so visits from friends should be kept short but they should still happen. It is important for him to still feel part of his peer group and the contact should be maintained wherever possible.

Letters are very welcome indeed at this stage, so if Tom's friends could be encouraged to drop the odd line to him, it would be very much appreciated. If one of Tom's family could scribe a letter back, this may encourage the communication to continue.

Membership of the ME Association's Young People's Group will be a lifeline for him to know that he is not alone in all of this. This group (see Useful Addresses) has pen friend and newsletter contacts.

Tom may feel more at ease with fellow ME sufferers, than with his old group of friends. Only another sufferer from ME really knows what he is going through. Tom may even imagine that his old friends are moving on while he is going backwards.

"I felt a real lack of confidence in myself. My IQ seemed to plummet, I couldn't plan an essay or process information. I'd end up in tears through the frustration of it. I had been used to doing difficult crosswords with my friends and now I could barely tackle a word search."　　　　　　　　　　　　　　**(Tom)**

It is only like this whilst you are feeling so ill. Back in Chapter 5, we found that there is no dementing process going on in your brain. When your health improves and your 'ferry boats' (neurotransmitters) are able to land once more in their own mooring place (receptors), then your memory and reasoning power will return.

Very gentle physiotherapy may be useful at this time, providing that the physiotherapist understands the limititations of ME and can visit the home. It would be detrimental for Tom to attempt a journey to hospital while he is at the severe stage of ME.

If he is in too much pain to be touched, a visit from an understanding physiotherapist can still be very helpful by instructing Tom's carers in the best way to move him from the bed to the toilet or into a chair. The carer's physical health is just as important as Tom's and the most obvious way of assisting a patient in and out of bed is often the wrong one. It feels most natural for the carer to bend over the bed and pull the patient towards them and up into a sitting position. The patient is then bear hugged and shuffled around, into the chair. This is the easiest way for the carer to put his or her back out, it is not the easiest way to manoeuvre a bedridden patient. Take advice, for the sake of everybody.

A physiotherapist who understands ME can suggest gentle muscle stretching exercises which can be carried out by Tom's carer at the best time of the day. Although he may feel ill and in pain all day, there is probably a particular time when the pain eases slightly. Very gradually, with patience, the movement will get easier and less painful. Dr Franklin explains:

> "Passive exercises from a physiotherapist should lead to gentle weight bearing and progressive movement should progress to slowly improved mobility. But it is important to recognise tiring or over use and to stop in good time."
>
> (Children With ME. Franklin)

Carina

Most of you, like Carina, will be at the Convalescent stage of ME, generally between 30% and 80% ability. At the lower end of the scale, Carina will probably be able to walk a little and be out of bed for much longer periods. Rest is still very important indeed as she will still feel very ill, although a few exercises and short walks into the fresh air should be encouraged. These short walks should be built up from a few steps. The temptation to 'just walk to the shop and back' when you have been bedridden for many weeks is overwhelming but must be checked. Carina's family will be delighted to see her back on her feet and Carina will want to please them further by walking a significant distance.

Dr Franklin would warn her to take:

> "extreme caution. Any excess exercise may cause a relapse
> to stage one."   (Children With ME. Franklin)

First thing in the morning Carina may continue to feel very poorly with her legs feeling as if they are encased in concrete but, increasingly, there will be times during the day when she feels a lot better. The headache may fade a little and her thinking become a little clearer. Then is the time for her to get her 'ferry boats' working again. Simple word searches and puzzles are useful as they can be done whilst resting on the settee.

Gradually, as Carina gets better, the symptoms will fade whilst she rests, sleeping patterns become more regular and although she will still find it difficult to wake her brain up in the morning, the periods of feeling better will get longer.

This is the difficult part of ME. Carina may feel that she can already see the top of the mountain but it may be just one of the many peaks that she comes across. The real physical and mental work of climbing the mountain has only really just started.

"The convalescence is the hardest bit - literally learning a new way of life in every aspect: study, socialising, exercise. Once you're mobile again, the support dies off as you can look deceptively well.

Oh yes - convalescence was when the problems truly started."   *(Carina)*

So what is convalescence? Years ago there were many convalescent homes in the country. Following a serious operation or illness, patients were encouraged to go and stay in these homes to recuperate. Away from the stresses of everyday life, it was an ideal situation in which to recover; gradually taking on more and more. Nowadays, patients are encouraged to get out of bed at the earliest opportunity following an operation and to pick up on life as soon as they can.

Gradually the need for convalescent homes decreased and

many of them closed down. The kind of care that these homes provided was just the type of care that Carina needs in her recovery from ME. She needs someone to help her to do all the things that she cannot yet manage and, at the same time, encourage her to build on what she can.

"I would like to be spirited away to a pressure free environment - a pretty cottage in a beautiful place with lots of fresh air. Someone there to help me gradually take control of my life without undue fussing."

One problem for Carina may be other people's perception of her. Once she can walk around or be seen outside of the house, other people, including her friends, will assume that she is well again - a bit tired still but almost recovered. Carina herself may have difficulty finding a balance between what she wants to do and what she can do.

"I found the in-between stage very difficult. I felt like doing things but didn't really have enough energy. I'd start something and not be able to finish it."

Learning that everything will get finished in time is an important lesson. Half an hour at a mental activity, perhaps writing a letter, should be followed by a restful activity such as listening to music. The letter can then be completed in the next half hour. Taken without a break, Carina's one hour activity of letter writing would probably not have been finished without the return of many ME symptoms - headache, painful eyes, sore neck, even painful leg muscles. By breaking up the activity, the letter can be written with Carina remaining relatively well.

She should not worry if the ideas in the letter wander a bit or that the writing is scrawly. If the letter is going to another ME sufferer then they'll understand anyway but if it is to one of her original friends, it may reinforce the problems of ME. While Carina is obviously feeling much better, her friends will perhaps realise that there is still a long way to go.

Educating her friends on how ME affects her will actually assist her recovery. If you think back to the time before you had ME, the illness may have been known to you but you may not have realised how limiting it was going to be in terms of socialising. Carina's friends want to see her getting better and 'going out' is seen as just that. They may be saying:

> "Mum says that she saw you out last week, so do you want to come to Trudy's birthday party with us? You can sit down all the time if you want."   or
> "You're looking ever so much better. How about coming out with us on Friday night. We're only going to the pub."

Carina will have forgotten the stimulating environment of going out with several young people, all talking at once. Even if she spent all the evening sitting down, the intense activity that her brain has to cope with, in noisy, busy surroundings, will exhaust her limited energy supply.

Healthy people have no problem with sitting up in a hard chair for several hours while their brain filters out any flashing lights from amusement machines or disco lights and the background noise. They can also tolerate alcohol to a fair degree.

Carina can't do any of the above. She will find her brain is unable to filter out the excess stimulation of lights, movement and noise and she may quickly get a pounding headache. Even a small glass of wine may bring on severe ME symptoms and I'm afraid to say, will continue to be the case for some considerable time to come.

Sitting upright in a chair is physically much more demanding than relaxing in an armchair or settee. All of these things together will rapidly use up Carina's energy, without her friends realising it. 'Trudy's party' or 'Only down the pub', can be an utterly exhausting way of spending two or three hours, especially if all her previous evenings have been spent watching TV on the settee.

She needs to gradually build up the time spent socialising in the same way as she builds up her physical activity. She needs to explain all this to her friends and ask one of her family to take her to the party or the pub in the evening but to call back in forty five minutes. To leave <u>before</u> she feels ill will ensure that she leaves sufficient energy to get home, relax and unwind before going to bed.

Even if she is sensible and leaves before she feels ill, the evening will probably still have taken its toll and she would be sensible to rest over the next two or three evenings. She may have been lucky and had no adverse reaction the following morning. Dangerously, Carina may feel that she 'got away with going out'. This may not be the case, and to explain why, let me use Dr Ho-Yen's analogy of equating energy to money.

Energy is money and one 'earns' money by resting. Healthy people are 'given' £1000 worth of energy every day whereas ME sufferers are 'given' only £100. This small amount should not only be spent wisely but the ME sufferer should also think about putting some in the bank.

"To make progress, patients have to go to bed with £10 unspent."   (Better Recovery from Viral Illness. Ho-Yen)

Carina went to the party or the pub with £135 worth of energy (£35 saved from previous days). Sensibly she left after 45 minutes, coming home with about £15 worth unspent. By the time she was tucked up in bed, she had probably spent a further £5, giving her the £10 to 'go to bed on'.

The next day she would have been given her usual £100 but a similar night out to the previous one would find her in an overdraft situation. She felt fine after the first night out with no 'overdraft' symptoms but the bank manager would have noticed that the account was nearly in the red!

"On Friday night you feel fine. Your friends phone you up and you go out with them. When you get back you realise that you have arranged to go out on Saturday night.

On Saturday you feel quite good, you go out at night and have a brilliant time, although you find it harder to walk towards the end of the night.

On Sunday you have to stay in bed all day because you have no energy and because you took too much out of yourself the previous evening.

You end up wishing that you hadn't gone out in the first place."

The danger of using the analogy of money in the bank is assuming that by resting more you can 'save' more. The more that is saved, the more you will be able to spend in one go. This ignores the advice given in Chapter 7 of this book which stresses the importance of balancing rest and activity.

Carina's friend, let's call her Ann, did not heed this advice. She was feeling a lot better, about 50-60% and didn't see the point of building up activity slowly. She knew that when she rested a lot more she would feel quite well in her self.

Ann's father was working in Spain for three months and asked her to join him once he had settled in, for a two months convalescent stay. The villa that he was staying in had a pool and a maid to get the meals. What a wonderful opportunity, thought Ann, although she was unsure whether she was well enough to travel. She decided that in order to have sufficient energy for the journey, she would rest up in bed for two weeks. At the end of this time she felt well and on realising that she 'didn't have a thing to wear on holiday', got up and went into town shopping.

Ann's muscles were unable to take the sudden surge of required energy and her brain couldn't take the massive increase in stimulation. On the brink of collapse, she took a cab home and went straight to bed. She was forced to stay there for the next four months, due to a very severe relapse, missing out entirely on the convalescent stay.

Carina is more sensible, she has worked out a management plan which incorporates plenty of rest with gently increasing activity. Using this she should be able to build up enough energy to have an enjoyable social life as her health improves.

Carina will gradually increase her study capabilities as she climbs the activity scale. By the time she is at the end of her convalescent period she is probably attending school/college/work part time.

Ricky

Ricky is now at 80% for most of the time; one or two bad days, especially if he over does things but in the main he rarely feels any severe symptoms when he is resting. He may have returned to school or college full time and although he still finds it tiring, by resting in the evenings and keeping the socialising down at weekends, he can mange fairly well.

Ricky is now able to take on a more structured exercise plan. Walking, swimming and cycling are all sensible activities to get involved with. Carefully and evenly the distances can be increased. The care that still needs to be taken is very frustrating and many of you will find this last 20% of the mountain, the most difficult to climb.

"I came to terms with the illness very easily, taking pleasure in simple things. Now that I have recovered sufficiently to be doing 'normal' things again, dipping my toes back in the water as it were, I find that the frustration is more difficult to handle. I'm mixing with healthy people once more and the feeling of being within touching distance of being able to do all that they do is hard.

It's not that I can't do what they do, it's having to always plan ahead, not doing too much two days running, being sensible about time. I just want to live life without having ME at the front of my mind all the time."

(Ricky)

If Ricky could turn these thoughts around a little, he may be able to feel the pleasure of being able to pick up on life again.

"I really appreciate doing things again for the first time. ME has given me a new and refreshing perspective on life. It has shown me what is important and how much there is to be grateful for - things that I would have taken for granted before."

Ricky may find that he has lost touch with the friends he had before and he is now looking for a way back in to a full social life.

"I would suggest contacting one of the youth organisations, you can usually find their address at the local library. This is great for any young person who has lost touch with their old circle of friends. A youth group can give you a range of friendships without the pressure of a 1:1 relationship. If club night is a 'bad

day' for you, you can miss going without feeling that
you're letting anybody down."

Ricky can now make plans for the future, although if he is sensible the goals will be achievable or the plan will have an opt-out clause attached.

"I've applied to go to university next year. If I am
honest I don't know if I'll be up to it but it's something
that I've always wanted to do and I want to feel that at
least I'm trying to achieve it.
It'll be a blow if I'm not well enough to go next year but
I'm pushing that thought to the back of my mind at the
moment.
If I have to face it I will - there's always the year after."

The possibility of relapses or slips down the mountain, are something that most of us will have to face at some time and planning for that possibility, even if it is pushed to the back of your mind, is a sensible move. ME is a relapsing and remitting (coming and going) illness and all three of our mountaineers should keep that in mind. If Tom, Carina and Ricky climb the mountain with care, taking note of sensible advice, they will keep the relapses to a minimum.

12

TRUST

If our three mountaineers are to be successful in scaling this rather difficult mountain they will need T-R-U-S-T.

Management and TRUST in ME

Dr David Bell, paediatrician at Harvard Medical School and specialist in ME writes about the management of ME:

> *"Management consists of a comprehensive treatment plan including medical, educational and psychosocial support with the aim of reducing both symptom and activity limitation."*
>
> *(CFS in Children. Bell)*

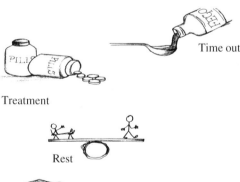

Time out

Treatment

Rest

Understanding

Support

A comprehensive treatment plan

Dr Bell's comprehensive treatment plan consists of eight parts:

A) Support and understanding from physicians and family

B) Frequent diagnostic re-evaluation

C) Rest and activity

D) Scholastic support

E) Psychologic Management

F) Improvement of sleep hygiene

G) Social management

H) Pharmacological treatment

I have incorporated these eight parts into five: **T-R-U-S-T**

Bell's H), F), B) into my **T** for **Treatment**:
pharmacological, sleep, re-evaluation of symptoms.

Bell's C)   into my **R** for **Rest and activity**:
cognitive behaviour therapy.

Bell's E)   into my **U** for **Understanding**:
from family and friends, counselling.

Bell's A), D)   into my **S** for **Support**:
from doctors, schools, financial.

Bell's G)   into my **T** for **Time Out**:
social time for all the family

Treatment

As yet there is no cure for ME,
it has to run its course.

In this book I have mentioned
the use of anti-depressants
(extra ferry boats) and if the
doctor suggests trying these,
it should be encouraged. These
can be useful in improving sleep
patterns, as well as helping with brain functioning in general.

There are other treatments which may reduce a few of the
unpleasant effects of ME, making the illness a little easier to
bear. I can recommend Dr Shepherd's book, 'Living With ME',
which has a large section on suggestions for relieving some of
the symptoms, although the main treatment is rest.

Any therapy which aids relaxation is useful, especially if you
have anxiety or panic attacks. This may sound strange since all
the ME patient seems to do all day is relax but there is a
difference between resting and relaxing.

You can rest but still feel very tense. If you are in a lot of
pain it is very difficult to relax. Tense muscles causes further
pain. The circle of pain - tension - further pain, needs to be
broken.

Some young people have found Aromatherapy oils beneficial for aiding relaxation. These can be added to bath water or
breathed in through vapours. Camomile and Lavender are said
to reduce tension and help sleep, although Camomile should
not be used during pregnancy. Geranium and Jasmin have an
anti-depressant and uplifting effect. High street shops sell the
burners and 'essential oils' but look carefully at the directions
on the bottle before purchasing. Some of the oils have a
stimulating effect and that's not what you want last thing at
night!

Chapter 6 mentions the importance of sleep and the difficulty that ME patients have in getting a regular pattern. If you find yourself sleeping most of the day and through the night, then one should allow this to continue. If, however, your sleep cycle is moving round, i.e sleeping during the day and awake most of the night, then you should be gently brought around to the family's sleep/wake cycle.

As with many other illnesses that have no magic cure, you may find many people arrive on your doorstep trying to 'help'. They've heard of someone, somewhere who did something weird and their ME disappeared!

I have heard of families who have sold their house and moved into rented accommodation in order to purchase extortionate alternative treatments from private medical centres.

Do think carefully before embarking on such a course, particularly if a lot of travelling is involved which exhausts the patient before they even start the treatment.

> *"People were always pushing magazine articles through my door about so called cures and how great the patients felt afterwards. I felt terribly guilty ignoring them.*
> *So many of them involved us travelling, which would have made her a whole lot worse. If the main treatment is rest, you can't then go whizzing around the country looking for a cure."*   *(Carer of 15yr old)*

There always seems to be someone, somewhere who did something
weird and their ME disappeared!

Pills and expensive mineral supplements often advertised in
the newspaper should be checked out with your doctor. Dr
Shepherd points out that the so-called natural medicines are
not always harmless. Germanium, for example, (not to be
confused with the essential oil 'Geranium') was targeted at
patients with ME and AIDS during 1989 with claims that it
would 'boost the immune system'.

"Germanium turned out to be potentially harmful and the
Department of Health had to withdraw it from sale following
reports of serious kidney damage." (Living With ME. Shepherd)

Personally, I find Evening Primrose Oil eases myalgia and the stronger pain killers will temporarily remove a headache. When I was at the severe (Toxic) stage of ME, anti-depressants helped with my coordination. Once I entered the Convalescent stage, I approached a local special school and asked if I could swim in their very warm hydrotherapy pool. Going once a week during their lunch hour, I gradually built up my strength from swimming a few strokes to a few slow lengths.

None of the above therapies did anything to alleviate the overwhelming fatigue. Only rest helps that!

Once you find the treatment that best suits your needs, trips to the doctor often decline. There seems little more that can be done and it's exhausting waiting around to be seen. However, your doctor needs to know how your illness is progressing, even if he or she doesn't seem on the face of it, particularly interested.

"Since many of the symptoms of CFS are present early in other disease states, periodic diagnostic re-evaluation is essential."   *(CFS in Children. Bell)*

Before you go to the doctor, make a copy of the Ability Scale in this book and note where you are and what you can manage to do, pointing out any differences from your previous visit. Ask the doctor to keep this with your medical records.

If there are any changes in the pattern of symptoms, these should be investigated with tests as necessary. If these come back negative then it has at least alerted the doctor to further symptoms connected with ME.

I am aware that many of you have had a less than sympathetic deal with your doctor but it is important for you to keep him or her informed of any other treatments that you decide to try. Remember that if any new treatment fails to work, or leaves you feeling worse, then it isn't easy having to return to your GP and eat humble pie. Your parents may even have to ask him or her to come out and see you. You don't need an 'atmosphere'!

Rest and Activity

"Without rest, recovery will not occur."

(Living With ME. Shepherd)

If you are at the same stage as Tom in the previous chapter, then bed rest is probably the order of the day. However, as soon as there is an indication of some improvement, this rest should be alternated with some small physical or mental activity.

In some cases, where the patient seems unable to reach the Convalescent stage, a stay in hospital may be suggested for Cognitive Behaviour Therapy (CBT). Diane Cox and Leslie Findley, working in The Oldchurch Hospital in Romford, Essex, have published their combined approach to treating ME by using CBT and graded activity (see References).

The base line of their work is for the patient and family to identify the best ways of managing and overcoming the illness (CBT) and then carry them out (graded activity).

"The therapist and patient work together to plan strategies to deal with clearly identified problems with the emphasis placed on self-help."

(Is CFS treatable in an NHS environment? Cox)

Emphasis is placed on the importance of balancing rest and effort, although once this balance is achieved, the activity is carried out every day.

"These activities are up or down graded dependent upon the effects on the patient, the main gauge being a change in symptoms in the following 24 hr period."   (Cox)

It could be argued that the suggestions for activity and rest found in this book are the same as those suggested by Cox and Findley. The only significant difference with CBT is the insistence that activity is carried out every day, albeit scaled down in the above hospital if it is found to be too severe.

Personally, I am almost into Recovery but I still have days when I wake up knowing that it will be a 'bad' day. If I push on with activities that I have planned, even if they are scaled down, I risk having several more 'bad' days. If I cancel that day and rest, I can be fairly sure that the next day will allow me to return to my usual level of activity. For those young people like Tom, the effect of pushing on with even scaled down activities could, I feel, delay his recovery.

However, I do believe that a balanced programme between rest and activity should be found and kept to <u>where</u> <u>possible</u>, especially for patients in the Convalescent stage. This balance can be sought from talking it through with your carer, together perhaps with a counsellor who understands the limitations of the illness.

However, rest should be the predominant factor in the treatment plan.

TREATMENT PLAN
At 30% ability, Carina's plan may be headed:

* 1) When will I take my <u>rest</u> periods and for how long?
* 2) What activities will I fit around my rest periods?

Gradually, as Carina comes to the end of her convalescent period her treatment plan will change to:

* 1) What <u>activity</u> will I do today and for how long?
* 2) When will I take my rest period?

Understanding

"I don't need people to fuss around. I don't need them necessarily to understand, I just want them to <u>realise.</u>"
(YP 18yrs)

Unless you have ME yourself it is very difficult to truly understand how the sufferer really feels. Therefore, perhaps we are asking too much of others to expect them to 'understand' but with the right knowledge we can help them to 'realise'. It is this knowledge that we can help to impart.

"I just wish more people knew about the illness."
(YP 15yrs)
You can help more people to know about the illness.

The two ME organisations, ME Association and Action for ME, have leaflets and booklets that go some way in explaining the problems of ME in children and are well worth getting hold of to distribute to your friends and relatives. Once the immediate family realise what the illness is and how best to deal with it, then they can begin to inform others.

Some young ME sufferers are having a hard time from their friends, merely because those friends don't understand.

"My friends are always ringing up and saying, 'You are lucky to be at home we had a really hard test this week,' or, 'I wish I could stay at home all the time and watch telly'. I get so fed up with it."   (YP 14yrs)

If brothers or sisters attend the same school as the sufferer they can sometimes help others to understand.

Kerry was fifteen when she wrote an article for the MIZZ magazine about ME, an extract of which is printed in Chapter 15. When she was first diagnosed the children at her school gave her a similarly bad time as the young person above. Kerry's twelve year old brother, David, wrote a short piece in her article which showed that as soon as he understood, he was able to help Kerry's friends and his own, to understand.

"Living with an ME sufferer is the weirdest thing I have ever experienced. No one knows what it's like and they don't understand the complications that are involved. I have to go to school and face loads of questions, and no one wants to know that Kerry isn't feeling any better.

At first I thought that it was a skiving act to get away from school - but when Kerry went to bed at 7.30pm and didn't wake up till 9am, had an afternoon sleep as well and then was still tired, I started to realise that there was something wrong. I thought that because she didn't look ill on the outside that it gave me the right to call her lazy but I was very wrong.

A specialist diagnosed ME and explained what it meant.

Now that I understand her illness I have to try to help her.
She gets lonely because she can't go out and see her friends. I try to keep her company but there isn't anything I can really do except be there for her if she needs me, which I'm not terribly good at.
If you know someone with ME, don't give up on them - try to help them instead."

(David. 12yr old brother)

I'm sure that when Kerry's family read what David had written they could reassure him that he was, in fact, very good at 'being there for her'. In fact Kerry's mother said that David had been Kerry's lifeline to the outside world, bringing in all the local young people's gossip.

Seeing David's thoughts on paper gave the family a chance to talk through with him his perception of Kerry's illness and for him to understand other people's.

It is often difficult for young people to tell their parents how they are coping emotionally with the illness. They know that their mum and dad are just as worried and don't want to burden them with more anxiety.

This attitude not only builds barriers between family members, it means that you are more likely to meet those trees of emotion more regularly.

Counselling can be of help; an objective, unconnected person, that will listen to everyone's point of view.

A good counsellor does not necessarily give advice but listens carefully and helps the client to make their own decisions.

"What would have helped me most would have been to have someone who I could have really talked to, telling them just how I felt. I had a wonderful supportive family but they just wanted to see me cheery all the time. I think it helped them through it, if I could stay positive."   *(YP 17yrs)*

Postal counselling can be helpful for the young sufferer that is house bound - see Useful Addresses. This involves the ME patient, or any of his or her family in writing to the counsellor over a period of three months or so. They will be encouraged to write about how they are coping with the illness, where they or the sufferer is on the Ability Scale and what the patient's treatment plan consists of.

The first few communications can sometimes be difficult, as with face to face counselling. It takes one or two letters to allow both parties to feel comfortable with the outcome.

Many young people find writing down their feelings much easier than talking about them. If advice is offered it can then be accepted, rejected or adapted to suit the person's own need, something that is more difficult with face to face counselling.

The questionnaires that were sent out in 1991 gave many people the opportunity to write down exactly how they felt about having ME. One young man filled in the back sheet which asked for further comments and then went on to write fifteen

more sides of A4 paper!
> *"I am not expecting you to reply to this but you have no idea what a relief it has been just writing all this down."*
> (YP 20yrs)

More often than not a serious illness draws families together but sometimes it pushes them apart while the different members of the family try to understand the illness and its effects.

> *"We discuss problems a lot less than we used to - each trying to cope with the problem in our own way and having nothing left over to help each other. There seems little time for togetherness any more."*
> (Carer of 18yr old)

Often poetry is an easier way of expressing just how you feel. You can then hand this over to someone for their comments:
> "Look what I've written."

It's an easier way into a discussion than saying:
> "Sit down, I want to tell you just how fed up I am."

Emma's mum sent the poem overleaf to me, saying how useful it had been for opening up a conversation and really finding out how Emma was feeling.

> *"It wasn't that she told me anything I didn't already know about her, but it was the fact that she actually volunteered the information and discussed it off her own back, without me having to keep asking her how she felt.*
> *It was very emotional for both of us and there were many tears and cuddles. I think it was a sort of therapy session for us, really, as we felt drained but a lot better*

afterwards.
Emma's a quiet child, very shy and I think she felt happier writing down her feelings, as opposed to talking about them."   *(Emma's mother)*

Emma's Poem:
The Sofa

I get up in the morning
And walk down the stairs.
Already I feel shattered,
And it's only nine o'clock.
I need to lay on the sofa.

I go into the kitchen
To get myself some breakfast.
I'm eating, it hurts my mouth, throat, stomach.
I'm fed up with the pain,
I need to lay on the sofa.

I must get dressed,
I need to go upstairs.
No energy, feeling exhausted,
Don't think I can do it -
I need to lay on the sofa.

I try to read my book,
Can't concentrate, well very little.
I'm bored, lonely, sad.
I want someone to talk to. I want a game of football -
                but
I need to lay on the sofa.

You look better today, they say with a grin
But I feel horrible, no energy,
Only pain in my neck, stomach, legs.
Will they ever understand that
I need to lay on the sofa!

Is it ever going to stop, I ask myself,
This hurt, depression, loneliness.
Don't give up hope they say, you'll feel better one day
But meantime, I think -
I need to lay on the sofa.

(Emma   13 yrs)

Support

From knowledge comes understanding - from understanding comes support. This support is needed from medical and educational workers.

*   Medical Support

More and more patients are now finding that their doctors are supportive during the series of laboratory tests, the diagnosis and the follow up period. By no means all, unfortunately, and it adds a great deal of unnecessary stress to find yourself involved in long discussions with your doctor.

If there is great scepticism with your own GP it is some-times helpful to change to another doctor, either within the practice or to a different surgery. It is worth asking the Practice Manager if any of the doctors have young patients with ME. Occasionally the local ME support group can give you the names of doctors who have been supportive to their members. In order to get the financial support that you are entitled to, you need your doctor to understand the limitations of ME. As we established under 'Treatment', your doctor does need to be kept informed of the progress of the illness.

*   **Educational Support**

I could fill the rest of this book with the varying tales of support, good, bad and non-existent from schools and colleges. There are stories where the schools have arranged for

the young sufferer to take examinations at home as well as giving them all the rest periods that they require during the examination.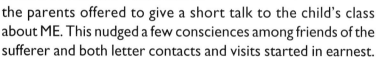

Some students have been regularly sent newsy letters from their old form group, even though they have been unable to attend for well over a year.

I heard of one case where one of the parents offered to give a short talk to the child's class about ME. This nudged a few consciences among friends of the sufferer and both letter contacts and visits started in earnest.

On the other hand, there are stories where the family have been threatened with court action if the child is not returned to school. These tales show the importance of getting medical support. Where there is no doubt about the illness and your doctor is fully informed about progress, support from other agencies will be much more forthcoming.

Between these two examples above lie the majority of young

people who may have been absent from school for some considerable time. If a long-term sick note has been sent by the doctor this is sometimes seen by the parents as all that needs to be done, especially if a home tutor is coming in. If the home tutor is in constant touch with your school then the contact between you and your school is kept alive and arrangements for you taking exams or returning to school can be discussed by the tutor.

Maybe you are still struggling to get a home tutor, or the tutor you do have has no contact with your school. If this is the case then it will probably be down to your parents to make regular contact with the school. They have to be persistent. Schools are such very busy places and your absence doesn't usually make the teacher's heart grow fonder. With the best will in the world, out of sight is often out of mind.

If your parent can make termly or half-termly visits to your form tutor, then everyone is kept up to date with progress.

With regular contact the provision of home tutoring and its link with the school becomes much easier. Most Comprehensive schools and some Grammer schools have a Special Needs department. The teachers in this department can often assist in any conversation with the LEA over home tuition.

Under the 1993 Education Bill the Local Education Authority (LEA) has a responsibility to provide education for a child that is unable to attend school (see Chapter 14), although the quality of that tuition does vary greatly from one area to another. In addition there is the added complication of who pays for the service.

Unless the school is in the private sector it will be run either by the LEA or it will be grant-maintained (GM). The LEA schools will have received a certain sum of money for each child in their school and if that child now requires education at home the school may be expected to make a contribution towards the cost of that home tuition. With the GM and private schools the home tutor will be paid directly from the school's budget and the parents may find that the school's understanding and support tails off as the allowance runs out.

The Advisory Centre for Education - ACE (see Useful Addresses) understands the limitations of ME and are an excellent scource of advice and informative books.

In the July 1993 edition of their bi-monthly newsletter 'ACE Bulletin', they focussed on the case of a twelve year old ME sufferer. This girl had been receiving home tuition from her grant-maintained school for a period of six weeks.

At this point it was discontinued as the school said it could no longer afford to provide the service and referred the parents to the LEA. ACE approached the Department of Education on behalf of the parents, who reiterated that Local Authorities were responsible for the provision of education for children otherwise than at school and that:

> "in exercising their power to provide home tuition to pupils registered at schools they must treat grant-maintained pupils no less favourably than LEA pupils."
>
> (Home Tuition - who pays? ACE Bulletin July 1993)

In situations where your parents are wanting the support of the authorities it is helpful for them to remain calm but persistent. They are advised to get as much written support as they can, from your doctor, school and advisory services.

Your name needs to be continually placed in front of those that are ultimately responsible, that is, the Local Education Authority.

* **Financial Support**

If young people are needing special care at home or have problems with mobility then there are financial benefits that can be claimed. The freephone Benefit Line 0800 882200 is there specifically for people with disabilities and give friendly help and advice.

The leaflets explaining these benefits can usually be picked up at a General Post Office, or will be sent to you, on request, from calling the above number. Other numbers are given in Useful Addresses.

Disability Living Allowance is available for anyone under the age of 65 years who needs:
   * *'help with getting around'*
                        (Mobility Allowance - Higher and Lower rates)
   or
   * *'help with personal care'*
                (Care Allowance - Higher, Middle and Lower rates)
   or
   * *'help with both of these'.*
   (ref. leaflet DS704. Disability Living Allowance. Benefits Agency)

Invalid Care Allowance may also be given if you, the patient, are eligible for DLA (Care) at the middle or higher rate, and the carer:
   * *'spends at least 35 hours a week looking after the patient'.*
      (ref. leaflet FB31. Caring for someone? Benefits Agency)

Income Support is available from the age of 16yrs:
'if the young person is incapable of work because of a mental or physical disability' and *'be likely to remain incapable for at least a year'*.

It is for those people who have not paid sufficient National Insurance contributions. Usually those of you who fell ill at the end of your schooling and have not yet worked.

(ref. leaflet IS20. Income Support. Benefits Agency)

Incapacity Benefit is the old 'Sickness Benefit' and will be paid to you if you have sufficient National Insurance contributions.

If you are unsure whether you qualify, the Benefits Agency should be able to check if you have enough N.I. credits. When you ring or write, they will need your National Insurance (NI) number.

Incapacity Benefit is presently paid on a three tier rate according to the length of your illness:
* *   First 28 weeks of sickness   - short term lower rate
* *   From weeks 29 to 52   - short term higher rate
* *   After one year   - long term rate

(ref. leaflet IB201. Incapacity Benefit. DSS & Benefits Agency)

If you are unsure whether you qualify for any of the above, the recommendation that comes from the Benefits Agency is:
'If you are unsure whether you qualify, apply anyway.'

Many of the above benefits are not dependent on income or savings.

There is sometimes a feeling of social stigma attached to

claiming benefits, especially if the family is managing without financial hardship. However, the following section, 'Time Out' suggests several ways of making the time pass a little quicker or life a little easier, and they all cost money.

If you are unable to take examinations at school, you may need rather costly correspondence courses later, such as those from the Open University. While you have been really ill and unable to spend anything at all, your 'benefit' fund may have accumulated. Having an available lump sum is a good incentive to thinking about an open learning opportunity, when you are feeling better.

One of my friends has had a computer bought for her and she is using her benefit to repay the loan, every week.

If you are getting Disability Living Allowance (Mobility) at the higher rate, then you may also qualify for an 'Orange Badge'. This entitles any car in which you are travelling to park close to amenities - even on yellow lines in some cases!

If you receive the lower rate DLA (Mobility), then your application needs the support of your doctor in order to qualify. This badge opens up many more opportunities for you to go out with your family and friends. Ring your local Social Security office and ask for a form for the Orange Badge Scheme.

Time Out

Most illnesses that are not life threatening, follow a clear pattern:

*   you get ill
*   stay indoors
*   feel better
*   go out again.

You tend to feel guilty if you go out before you are better.

ME doesn't follow the pattern of 'feel better' then 'go outside', you go out before you get better and then feel guilty about being seen out.

> *"I felt I couldn't even let her walk down to the postbox incase her friends saw her and said that she ought to be back at school."*   *(Carer of 13yr old)*

Perhaps the friends of the thirteen year old girl above need to see the Ability Scale and realise that trips out are a part of her recovery process.

Dr Bell feels that any management plan should take social functioning into account. With a long term illness such as ME it is so easy for the patient to slip into a permanent state of social isolation.

> "The goal is to maintain social contact so that when recovery occurs social isolation is not a permanent sequelae(symptom following a disease)."   *(CFS in Children. Bell)*

'Time Out' is not meant to imply that we should be thinking of a visit to the local football match or joining in a game of ten pin bowling.

It means that, despite the illness, we mustn't lose sight of our need for a regular dose of 'feel good factor' - Fego. Everyone needs some time out of ME even if it's only fifteen minutes worth per day; any small activity that is not overtaxing but allows you to push ME to the back of your mind for a short while. It can be passive listening to your favourite music, five minutes playing the piano or finding the next piece in the jigsaw. Perhaps you need to ask someone to count all the pieces before you start. It would do you no good at all to spend two hours looking for the very piece that's disappeared up the vacuum cleaner!

"Two doses of 'Feel Good Factor' every day"

Maintaining friendships becomes very difficult but hired videos and board or computer games can sometimes attract friends in. Try not to leave too long a time lag between contacts. The longer the absence the more difficult it becomes to pick up the friendship again.

"It was so difficult to talk to my friends when I hadn't seen them for so long. I didn't know what to say. Six months before we seemed to talk for hours and hours."

(YP 14 yrs)

Soon into the early Convalescent stage, boredom sets in: wanting to do something different but having no energy with which to do it!

Membership of an organisation can sometimes be the incentive to do something useful. Maybe the club will have some easy job that needs doing, designing a poster for the next meeting or putting newsletters into envelopes, for example. The National Council for Voluntary Youth Services may be able to put you in touch with a local group (see Useful Addresses). The ME Association has a young people's group with a penpal section and a newsletter that always needs features and articles.

The following list gives you a few more ideas for giving yourself a dose of Fego, the 'feel good factor':

* Designing your own greeting cards - computer generated or embroidered

* Designing and swapping wordsearches and crossword puzzles

* Making toys

* Jigsaws

* Writing poetry

* Learning to play a keyboard

* Learning a foreign language through tapes.

All of these activities will give Carina a dose or two of Fego, no matter how short a time she spends on them but they must be able to be put down and picked up to fit in with how she is feeling.

Tom will probably be saying, "That is all very well but I spend most of my time in bed, how do I get a dose of Fego?" This list gives a few ideas to make life easier for Tom but some are costly:

* Remote controlled TV

* Remote controlled video recorder

* Mobile or cordless phone

* Magazines and comics

* Tape recorder

* Simple travel games

* Laptop computer or lightweight word processor.

It is possible for Tom to get his own dose of Fego through achievement, even if he has been in bed for a long time. If he can write a diary, or even dictate for someone to scribe, he can record what he has done that day, small though it may be.

'I learnt to say good morning in Spanish today' is encouraging and can be built on. It may have only taken ten minutes but something was achieved that day.

Some young people who don't write a diary have an achievement chart that they put on their bedroom wall. ME makes such slow progress that you sometimes think you haven't moved at all - your chart can tell you otherwise!

> *"Spending most of the day on the settee, I felt really useless. Everyone was getting on with their lives and I was stuck. So I asked for a foreign language course for my birthday. It took me nearly two years to get through it, but it was brilliant, no pressure, no competition."*
> *(YP 16yrs)*

Of course you don't have to learn a foreign language to get a dose of Fego. If you haven't been out of the house for weeks or months, then a <u>short</u> car ride or trip into the park in a wheelchair can be very beneficial and certainly something to be written on the achievement chart.

There are many young people that put up their hands in horror at the thought of being pushed around in a wheelchair but once the first trip has been made, most patients see the freedom that comes with it.

> *"I told mum that I didn't want a wheelchair but she got me one anyway. I was really mad at her but my brother took me round the garden just to try it out and it felt OK. I now think it's great. It means that I can choose all my own Christmas and birthday presents<u>and</u> new clothes!"*
> *(YP 15yrs)*

Be warned, though, don't get hooked on Fego. Only a short trip in the car or wheelchair at first. It is <u>very</u> tiring sitting upright, whilst dealing with bends in the road or bumps on the path, together with the mental stimulation of being outside.

Try sitting in the wheelchair at home for about half an hour at first. If you can manage that, then you can probably manage a ten minute push along a pathway.

In addition to you needing 'Time Out', it is just as important for your carer to have a break. Parents often think that they are the only ones who can look after their child. The young person may even try and tell them that, thereby adding to their guilt of leaving the patient with someone else.

"She used to go to her grandparents but they didn't understand how limited she was. So now I don't get a break at all. I have to cope for 24 hours a day, 7 days a week. I have no one to talk to."   *(Carer of 13yr old)*

"I can't go out and leave him when he is in so much pain. We did have a nurse in for a while to help him with washing and toileting but he said she caused him more symptoms so I do it all now.
Nobody likes to go out, even his sister, as she says she feels guilty doing things that our son cannot do."
(Carer of 19yr old)

Your carer's physical and mental health is important.
"It is difficult to get enough physical exercise, living at the pace of the sufferer."   *(Carer of 11yr old)*

"I hadn't realised how dependent I had become on knowing how she was at all times of the day."
(Carer of 16yr old)

Carers need to find sometime in the week that is just for them, a game of badminton or a pub meal, for example. This may mean having to organise a friend to be with their child but before they do that they should make sure that the patient really does need constant attention.

"My mum felt I couldn't ever be left. I didn't like to tell her that I'd have appreciated some time on my own."

(YP 18yrs)

This, of course, takes us back to the need for good communication and understanding.

It helps if those around you understand the comprehensive treatment plan, T-R-U-S-T, and the importance of a regular dose of Fego. Each member of the family can then encourage the other to take it.

13

BASE CAMP

Once you start to feel a little better, physically and emotionally, you should be ready to start the climb towards recovery. This happens at any stage, Toxic, Convalescence or Recovery. You're through the forest and are able to recognise any of the emotional trees, should you meet them again on your journey. You've accepted the present limitations that ME presents and understand the treatment plan: T-R-U-S-T. You now need to establish what you can manage to do, physically and mentally; to do this you need to get yourself to B-A-S-E C-A-M-P.

If you are still struggling emotionally to come to terms with the illness or if you are presently on the way down, then a perusal of the previous chapters might help you through. There is no rush, use the time to rest until you are ready to move on.

Rest First then:

Build
Activity
Slowly and
Evenly

Communicate
And
Monitor
Progress

Base Line

In order to build on your activity you need to establish what you can manage to do easily, i.e find your base line. I am using the word activity where others might use exercise and it should be taken to mean anything that uses physical or mental energy.

For Tom, in the Toxic stage of ME, activity may mean sitting up in bed instead of lying down; reading a book or drawing for five minutes. For Ricky, in the Recovery stage, it may be a half day at school/college or a swim in the local pool.

Make a note (or ask someone else to jot down) whatever it is that you can manage, no matter how small. Keep a diary for two or three weeks. It will take at least this long to find a pattern; often much longer.

The following three diaries have been condensed from those that I have received, in order to make it less tedious to read. The one week that is mentioned is really made up of four, and sometimes eight, weeks.

Tom

Tom may think that his activity is so insignificant that it doesn't count - "did nothing yesterday, did the same today!"

There will be some time in the day, I feel sure, when Tom sits in a chair while his bed is made or is propped up in bed to entertain a friend.

These are all activities and should be noted down, together with how long it took and how he felt at the end of it.

TOM'S DIARY might read:

MON: Sat in bedside chair 10 mins. Nice to return to bed.

TUES: Sat in bedside chair 10 mins. Just about right - not too tired.

WED: Sat in chair 10 mins. David came round and lent me his video. I was in bed. He stayed chatting for 30 mins. Very, very tired when he left. Bad headache.

THU: Bad headache all day. Felt really ill. Sat in chair 2 mins. Very tired all day.

FRI: Better today. Sat in bedside chair for 15 mins.

At the end of the week, Tom and his family can look at what he did: ten minutes in the chair seemed to be about right. When he felt a bit better, he extended it to fifteen minutes and when he was really poorly he cut it down to two.

When his friend came round it was clearly too much. Tom felt very tired when he left and it gave him worse symptoms the following day. But his friend, David, must not be put off. One of Tom's family needs to explain to David that his visit was very much appreciated but perhaps next time he ought to make it a fifteen minute call as Tom was too tired after the half hour stay.

Tom's base line is:
10 minutes in a bedside chair OR
15 minutes of a friend visiting and 2 minutes in a bedside chair.

Carina

A sensible mountaineer will not break out into a run while they are on a difficult part of a mountain. If they did they would probably find themselves tumbling back down the mountain. In the same way, Carina should take care to 'climb' slowly and evenly. Patients and their families are often tempted to plan activities that are too active, too soon. Carina needs to keep a careful account of what she does day by day.

CARINA'S DIARY might read:

MON: am. Downstairs at 10.30. TV 'til 12.30.
Made lunch for mum 20 mins.
pm. 1hr rest. Walk 10 mins. Homework half hour.
evening. Bed at 10. Feel good.

TUES: am. Downstairs at 10.30. TV 'til 12.30.
Made lunch 20 mins. Wrote letter 30 mins.
pm. No rest. Took walk early 10 mins.
Sara came for one hour.
evening. Tried homework 15 mins - too tired.
Bed early.

WED: am. Bed 'til 12.00. Made lunch 20mins
pm. 2hr rest. Short walk 5 mins.
evening. TV. Felt tired and achey today.

THU: am Up 10.30 - wrote letter 30mins.
Early walk 10 mins.
pm. 1hr rest. Homework 15 mins.
Sara came for 30mins.
evening. TV. Felt good today.

FRI: am. Up at 10. Home Tutor 1 hour.
pm. 1hr rest. Walk 10 mins.
evening. Computer game with brother 40mins.
Good day.

Looking back at this diary you can see that on Monday Carina felt well on the activity that she managed. On Tuesday she added writing a letter, a friend visiting <u>and</u> she skipped her rest. I'm not surprised that she was too tired to do any homework in the evening. Luckily, by going to bed early and getting up late on Wednesday, plus having a longer afternoon rest, she didn't suffer too much. She was more sensible on Thursday by shifting things around in order to fit the rest in. She is sensible to arrange her friend's visit on Tuesday and Thursday, leaving the weekend activities to settle and it leaves Friday free for the Home Tutor.

Carina's base line is threefold:
    Writing a letter OR making lunch.
    1 hour pm rest. 10 minute walk.
    Friend visiting 30 mins and Homework 30 mins OR Home Tuition 1 hour.

This is much more comprehensive than Tom's base line. It should incorporate several small and varied activities. As Carina comes to the end of her Convalescent stage, the activities will have grown in size and the time taken will be longer.

Ricky

In the Recovery stage, many young people are retrieving their education by attending school or college part-time or taking open learning correspondence courses.

While they are using more mental energy, their physical activity may be limited. Ricky should ensure that he continues to balance his base line with both physical and mental activity.

RICKY'S DIARY might read:

MON: am. School 1½ hour. Rest over lunch.
pm. Homework 1 hour. Walk dog 10 mins. TV 2hrs
evening. Friends over to watch video 2 hours. Felt OK.

TUES: am. Up 10.30. TV. Walk dog 10 mins.
pm. School 2 hours. Rest.
evening. Homework. TV. A bit tired today.

WED: am. School 3 hours. Rest.
pm. Walk dog 20 mins. Friends over for 2 hours.
evening. Homework 30 mins. Bed early.
Very tired but my head is still buzzing.

THU: am. Missed school - too tired. Up at lunch time.
pm. TV. Walked dog 5 mins.
evening. TV. Bed early. Bad day today.

FRI: am. Up 10.30. TV. Walked dog ½ hour.
pm. School 1 hour. Rest.
evening. To friend's house 1 hour.
Better day today, glad I rested yesterday.

For the most part, Ricky is carefully balancing his mental and physical activity. Dogs need regular exercise, as does Ricky, so it's helpful to put the two needs together. It's not easy to keep to a regular daily swim or cycle ride, there always seems to be a reason why it can be put off until the next day, not so with walking the dog!

Ricky's diary shows that he sensibly cancelled Thursday and he cut his walk down to 5 minutes when he felt ill (dogs soon get the hang of this!). To have gone to school regardless of how he felt may have meant him having many 'bad' days. As it was he was able to resume his previous level of activity on Friday.

If he looks carefully at Wednesday's entry, he can see the possible reason for feeling ill on Thursday. Wednesday is the fullest school day - all morning - which means getting up about two hours earlier than usual. In addition, he has friends over for two hours and still has homework to do in the evening. No wonder his head was buzzing. He probably had a real problem sleeping even though he felt so tired.

Ricky's base line is:
  School/Homework 2 hours
  Walk dog 20 mins
  Being with friends 1 hour

A smaller number of activities, perhaps, than Carina but Ricky can spend much longer at them.

*   *   *

Once the base line has been established the activities can be swapped around when necessary. Less time on academic study could mean a longer walk or more time with friends. If there is a busy day at school and homework to do, then friends should be put off until the next day.

Over the weeks and months, the base line can be extended but mental and physical activity should be built up evenly where possible - more school work and then a slightly longer walk - that will please Ricky's dog!

Build
Activity
Slowly and
Evenly

This all sounds very easy and logical but often ME doesn't fit an easy and logical pattern. It may not be a simple, steady climb up the mountain for you; finding base camp and away you go. The strategies that you decided upon may fail. There may be a downward path to travel before you can go up again. You may find that your journey on this downward path is more like a high speed tumble and your body really suffers from it when you finally stop falling.

This is really disappointing and intensely frustrating but perfectly normal. Look back at your diary to see if you can find a reason for the fall. If you can't, accept it as part of the illness and re-evaluate your activity path to suit your present base line. If you meet any of the emotional trees on the way, don't worry, identify them, accept them and pass on by.

Communicate

Some of the previous chapters have stressed the importance of communication between all the family members but I make no apology for mentioning it again.

All your family will climb at least part of the mountain with you. Like any good mountaineering team everyone should be communicating with each other, supporting and encouraging at every opportunity.

Your route to recovery will be bumpy. Like the real mountaineers, as things change, you may have to alter a previously designed route: timescales may have to be thought out again and discussion will be needed on the best way forward.

Your primary carer will probably be the person taking the main decisions while you are feeling very ill but it is important for you to be brought into discussions about the 'climb' as often as possible. The relationship between the primary carer and yourself becomes a very intense one as you are usually side by side on the mountain, going all the way up to the top together. You will share all the slips and tumbles along the way; share in the exhilaration of reaching new heights; share in the disappointment of realising that the real peak is still some way off.

"When she is happy and doing well, I feel happy but when she's low, I am too. I often think I ought to try and hide this sadness and be strong for her at that time."
(Carer of 15 yr old)

When you are both so closely involved with the illness it is understandable for patient and carer to shadow each other's emotions. If either party tries to hide their feelings of disappointment during the 'bad' days it is usually detected. For the patient particularly, they are left feeling guilty about being poorly again.

"Mum used to skip around my bedroom when I had an off day. It was as if she was making up for the energy that I didn't have. I know she thought it was for the best but I felt even more that it should be me skipping around and not her."
(YP 16yrs)

Both parties are left feeling that they have let the other down in some way. This is why communication is so important. Patients and carers have every right to their varying moods but don't be left having to guess how the other person is feeling.

"Children seem to know most things about what is going on and they are scared if things are not discussed openly.
We tried to make simple statements with quiet certainty, even on touchy subjects. As she has grown older we

have let the complications drift into our discussions and concentrated on letting her take part in finding constructive solutions.

We have had a rule that we must be prepared to talk about anything she took up - even things like 'Yes, I sometimes feel angry at having to straighten up after you, even though I know you cannot do it yourself just now. That is because I am not perfect and I get tired and frustrated sometimes, just like everyone else, just like you'."   *(Carer of 12 yr old)*

Monitor progress

Progress is very slow, we all know that, I'm sure. When you have a 'bad' day it seems to be one step forward and one step back and you're getting nowhere. However, if you were to look back over a longer period you may be able to see that some progress has been made.

If it hasn't you may be able to see the reason why by looking at your diary. However, even seeing some progress, you may still be viewing the 'bad' days as a step back. By putting a numerical score against your activity, and marking it on a graph week by week, the 'bad' days are no longer 'steps backwards'. They become part of the progression towards getting better. Gradual progress can be seen over the months as the graphed line creeps gradually upwards.

Another reason for monitoring your activity if you are a female, is to note any regular, monthly, cyclical changes. There is a feeling amongst some doctors that changes in oestrogen levels may be intensifying or even causing ME symptoms. There have been stories about some improvement seen in teenagers when they are put on the contraceptive pill and it is well known that women who suffer from ME feel a lot better during pregnancy when their oestrogen levels are changed.

The best way to be sure about changes in your symptoms is to monitor them. The best way to record that monitoring process is to draw a graph.

The best way to record that monitoring process is to draw a graph.

Besides the medical and emotional advantages of monitoring gradual progress, it also enables your carer to know how you're feeling without having to keep asking.

"There were times when I have put too much pressure on him - go for a walk, try school - when he was really not up to it and then we got angry with each other. But he won't tell me how he feels, I have to keep asking and he just says 'alright I suppose'." (Carer of 13 yr old)

How can we put a numerical score on 'walking the dog' or 'having a friend around'? It's fairly easy. Over the past year I have been sending out Activity Diaries to young people with ME who volunteered to help me. From these, I have devised a scoring system; one that you could use as it stands or adapt to suit your way of life. At the back of the book you will find a few pages set out as graph paper for you to use.

Activity Score

The following scale, although being rather general, makes an attempt at scoring activity.

To begin with, I rate different activities on a scale from 1 - 5. This scale is not fixed and should be adjusted according to other factors.

I have, for example, rated a trip out in a wheelchair at 2 but that would be a quiet trip in the park or out in the country. If that trip out is in a busy town centre with lots of mental stimulation and bumps up and down steps, then you would probably want to increase the rating to 2.5 or even 3. It is your activity and you know how much it takes out of you. Talk it over with your carer and come up with an activity rating between you.

To arrive at an Activity Score you need to multiply the rating by the time it took to carry out that activity.

As an example, let's assume that you agree with me and rate 'making lunch' at 2. In order to arrive at an Activity Score you need to multiply the 2 by the number of minutes that it took you to make that lunch, say 15 minutes.

$2 \times 15 = 30.$

30 is the Activity Score for making lunch.

Below is a suggested scale to rate your activity:

Activity Rate

ACTIVITY	RATE
Sitting up or out of bed watching TV. Listening to music, reading magazines etc.	1
Car/Wheelchair ride. Making simple lunch or tea. Writing letters/drawing/computer games. Gentle stretching exercises.	2
<u>Gentle</u> walking/swimming/cycling. Easy housework (dusting/tidying room).	3
Being in a stimulating environment, such as walking around town, visiting relatives or having friends around. Studying at home/Homework.	4
Any busy activity - out with friends, supermarket shopping, etc. Studying at school/college.	5

Once you have a rating scale from one to five, similar to that above, look at your diary to see how long you spent on each <u>significant</u> activity.

Sitting up watching TV would not be significant for Carina, because it would be something that she did most days for a long time. It would, however, be very significant to Tom, who is usually lying flat, not being able to watch the television at all.

Therefore Tom would rate the time he spent watching TV, Carina would not.

Let's score Tom and Carina's activity using just those activities from their diaries that are significant for them. I've left some of Carina's scoring for you - see how you get on.

Tom's Activity Score

	ACTIVITY	TIME	RATE	SCORE
MON:	Sat in bedside chair	10 mins.	1	10x1 = 10
TUES:	Sat in bedside chair	10 mins.	1	10x1 = 10
WED :	Sat in chair	10 mins.	1	10x1 = 10)
	David came round.	30 mins.	4	30x4 = 120)
				130
THU:	Sat in chair	2 mins.	1	2x1 = 2
FRI :	Sat in bedside chair	15 mins.	1	15x1 = 15

Total score for the week =   167

Do you remember, a few pages back, when you read Tom's diary? He had written about his bad headache on the Thursday and that he couldn't sit out of bed because he felt so ill. I explained that it could have been because of overdoing things the day before.

By scoring the activity, it is even clearer to see how he exceeded his base line on the Wednesday. Ten minutes in the chair was Tom's base line, which had an activity score of 10. It was suggested that if his friend visited again, it should be for 15 minutes only, and Tom only sit out in a chair for 2 minutes, thereby giving an activity score of 62. Much better than 130!

Carina's Activity Score

	ACTIVITY	TIME	RATE	SCORE
MON:	am. Made lunch	20 mins.	2	20x2 = 40
	pm. Walk	10 mins.	3	10x3 = 30
	even. Homework	30 mins.	4	30x4 =<u>120</u>
				190
TUES:	am. Made lunch	20 mins.	2	20x2 = 40
	Wrote letter	30 mins	2	30x2 = 60
	pm. Walk	10 mins	3	10x3 = 30
	Sara came	60 mins	4	60x4 =240
	even. Homework	15 mins	4	15x4 = <u>60</u>
				430
WED:	am. Made lunch	20 mins	_	20x_ = __
	pm. Short walk	5 mins	3	__x3 = __
				__
THU:	am. Wrote letter	30 mins	_	_x__ = __
	Early walk	10 mins.	_	_x__ = __
	pm. Homework	15 mins.	_	_x__ = __
	Sara came	30 mins	_	_x__ = __
				__
FRI:	am. Home Tutor	60 mins	4	__x4 = __
	pm. Walk	10 mins	_	10x__ = __
	even Comp game	40 mins	_	40x__ = __

Total score for the week = _____ 1295

These scores can now be graphed to show the ups and downs. Obviously you won't see any progression over one week but if you score for one month and then again in a few months time, you should see the activity score increase.

Tom's Activity Graph

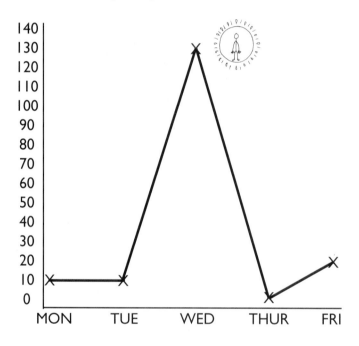

'Don't Exercise' warning light

Do you remember, at the end of Chapter 7 - Muscles and Exercise - I suggested that it would be very useful to have a 'Don't Exercise' warning light in our head to prevent us from doing too much? By keeping an eye on your activity score, week by week or even day by day, you should be able to see when the warning light will start to flash.

Carina's Activity Graph

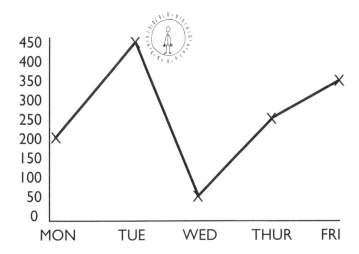

If you look at Tom's graph, you will see a band, between 5 and 20, within which he can manage without too many problems.

Once he steps out of that band, as on Wednesday when his friend came round, the warning light should flash!

Carina's, band is probably between 150 and 350, hence the warning light over Tuesday's score.

Any increase in her scoring should have been kept below 400 if possible. Had she scaled down her other activities on Tuesday she may have got away with her friend's one hour visit. As it was, she scored 430 and the warning light flashed.

You can follow Tom or Carina's example by scoring your activity over a month and plotting the scores on to a graph. You should then be able to see your base line and a band of activity, within which you can function fairly well.

Build slowly and evenly

When you feel capable of increasing your score, do so gently and give yourself the next day or two at the previous level to make sure that it hasn't meant an increase in symptoms.

Tom may be able to sit out of bed for 15 minutes on a really good day. Before he builds this up to 20 minutes he should build up the other days to 15 minutes. Tom's previous base line was '10mins in a bedside chair', Once this reads '15mins in a chair' he can then try 20 minutes out of a bed on a good day.

When this activity is plotted over a matter of weeks, Tom can really see the graph rising. The bad days all become part of getting better. Without this positive image he would be tempted to think, *'I'm not getting any better, I can still only sit out of bed for a few minutes'.*

You can plot your own graph on the pages that are set out for you at the end of the book.

The **BASE CAMP**, then, is the place to plan your climb.

Establish your base line and then:
>**B**uild on that
>**A**ctivity,
>**S**lowly and
>**E**venly.

>**C**ommunicate with each other
>**A**nd
>**M**onitor your
>**P**rogress as you go.

14

Education

In the last chapter we learned how to find our base line for activity and then how to increase it slowly and evenly. Returning to your education or training should be done in the same way. You can't expect your legs to suddenly walk you half a mile when you have been in bed or on the settee for so long. In the same way you can't expect your mental abilities to allow you to concentrate for long periods on a sudden return to school or college.

The environment is stressful. Step inside the school/college building, especially at change of lessons, and allow your senses to take in all the stimuli - crowds, movement and SO MUCH NOISE! Stressful environments draw on our meagre supplies of energy before we even think about carrying a heavy bag around and sitting up for an extended period on a hard chair, or even worse, a science stool! All this and the brain hasn't even started listening to and assimilating information.

Education, like physical activity, needs to be built slowly. If you have fallen right back to 0% on the Ability Scale then any form of concentration is very difficult indeed. You may be unable to remember simple things like telephone numbers or even the names of your friends (very embarrassing). Doing any form of mental arithmetic is completely out of the question.

Where to start?

Education is not possible at 0% but when will it be possible? A start has to be made to retrieve your education at some point.

Assimilating any new information when you are still lost in the forest of emotions is rather difficult. It might be better to wait until you've found the base camp and are more prepared to take stock of what you can manage. Don't think, though, that education is just learning from a tutor and doing work sheets and mental exercises. It can be as simple as writing a few sentences for a letter, a word search or a quiet box game. Any of these activities will nudge your brain back into action, even doing them for two or three minutes. The time taken doesn't matter.

One easy way for you to start picking up your education is right there in your room in front of a television. If there's a programme that interests you - no matter what it is - use it as a 'project' and think carefully about what it's trying to say in terms of social or environmental issues. If it's a serial, write, or just think about a 'what happened next' scenario; think about any historical or geographical issues that might come up in the programme. The possibilities are endless.

When you are well enough to have a home tutor, this interest that you have started is something to talk about and maybe develop. You may be unfortunate enough to have a tutor who seems to have little idea of how to educate a sufferer from ME and by having something already started, it might help the first tentative lessons.

"The first home tutor that we had was horrendous. She never liaised with the school and left it to us to decide what Robert wanted to learn but we had no idea. He ended up being left with a whole pile of boring work sheets to do."   *(Carer of 10 year old)*

Home Tuition

"TODAY, WE'RE GOING TO LEARN ABOUT M.E."...

The Ability Scale suggests that home tuition may be useful when you are around 40% able. Obviously this is a generalisation but some structured mental tasks should be considered around this time.

If the contact between your parents and the school has been patchy up to this point, it is worth them renewing their acquaintance. Obtaining a home tutor easily, seems to vary very much on where you live and it is important to have the school on your side, even though it is the Local Education Authority (LEA) that are ultimately responsible for providing the tutor.

In some areas, obtaining a home tutor is easy. A meeting at the school, often with the Education Welfare Officer (EWO), and a letter from your doctor, means a tutor quickly appearing on your doorstep and the process has begun.

In other areas it is a real battle with the authorities for your share of the Special Needs budget held at County Hall. It is therefore sensible to start the ball rolling as soon as you are able to concentrate for a short time as it could mean several months wait before anything happens. If you wait until you are feeling much better, you may look as if you are recovered and then pressure may be put on you to return to full time school too soon.

If problems are looming on the horizon it would be useful for your parents to get a copy of the government circular number 12/94, issued jointly by the Departments of Education and Health. The circular is called 'The Education of Sick Children' and can be obtained from your local reference library. In summary, it puts the duty of providing education otherwise than at school firmly on the LEA, and stresses the need for continuity in education for the sick child:

> *"Regarding home tuition, guidance is offered on the importance of LEA policies and continuity, on good practice in provision and on effective links between the home tuition service and the mainstream school."*
>
> *(The Education of Sick Children. 1994)*

Seeing it in print does not, of course, mean that it happens! The National Association for the Education of Sick Children (NAESC - see Useful Addresses) have expressed concern that despite the 1993 Education Act making provision for sick children statutory, the lack of specific funding means many local authorities are failing to make adequate provision. In their October '94 newsletter they point out some of the realities of educating sick children at home:

> *"Education is broader than coverage of what might be missed. It involves re-establishing the desire and ability to learn."*
>
> *(Editorial. NAESC Newsletter Oct 1994)*

Statementing

The authorities may be anxious for you to be 'statemented' before a home tutor can be arranged. This means putting the your needs down in a formal 'statement', which includes reports from different professionals: teachers, doctors, educational psychologists plus your parents. The procedure is very long winded and can take well over six months - eighteen months is not unheard of!

As a former head of a large Special Needs department in a comprehensive school, I do not see how ME really fits in with statementing. If you have ME your needs tend to vary month by month if not hour by hour. Therefore, how can you arrive at a conclusion about a child's needs for the coming year? Most statements do not carry provisos for any improvement or retardation that may happen over the year, merely what the child needs on the particular day of receiving the reports.

However, it's not all bad news. If you do go through a statementing process - not painful at all, incidently - and your parents approve of its contents (they can appeal if they're not happy), exemption from exams and general resources are easier to get. County Hall apply for funds based on the number of statemented children within their authority, plus any others that need it.

If you are not statemented you come under the 'others' and you may be told that there is no more money left for them to pay a home tutor.

Allocation of time

The amount of time that a tutor visits you, depends upon where you live. From information received in the first half of 1994, the NAESC had a directory published (see References), showing the different home tuition arrangements of 116 LEAs. It shows that most areas allocate five hours per week; one or two areas as low as two hours and a few rising to ten hours per week.

Five hours doesn't sound very much but even thirty minutes at one session can be very exhausting and certainly far more intense than a pupil experiences in school.

Unless you have no option, do not be tempted to accept your allocation of time in one block.

> *"To begin with, the tutor wanted to come once a week for her full allocation of two hours. It was difficult to make her understand that it would be far too much for him in one go."*   *(Carer of 14 year old)*

Neither should you feel obliged to take their full allocation of, say, five hours at the start. It is beneficial to begin slowly; ask to start with two hours. Even two hours needs to be built up slowly. An ideal arrangement might be:

* starting off with twice a week for half an hour,
* building to three sessions for half an hour,
* followed by two at three quarters of an hour and one at the half hour.

Don't lose sight of the fact that this might be the first pupil the tutor has ever had with ME and may not like to enquire too deeply into the illness. Have plenty of leaflets and information to give them that they can take away and absorb.

Two excellent publications are 'Guidelines for Schools' edited by Jane Colby, available from Action for ME, and 'The Education of Young People with ME', available from ME Association (see Useful Addresses).

Once home tuition has started, it is likely to continue for some considerable time. For you to have such regular, close contact with one person, for an extended time, means that your two temperaments must 'click'. Personality clashes can, for the most part, be avoided in a classroom, not so in a 1:1 situation!

"We've had a lot of experience with home tutors as my child has been ill for nearly five years. Some have been very good but we had two that were not at all suitable and once the visits have officially started it is very difficult to change that tutor.

What we do now, when a new tutor phones up to make arrangements, we suggest that they come round first to meet the child and have a cup of tea with us. That allows us to interview them. After all, they're going to be visiting your home on a regular basis, often allowing you to go out and leave them alone. You need to be sure. The 'cuppa' visit isn't always received very well because the tutor only gets paid after a contract has been agreed. But you need to assess them before the contract is signed." **(Carer of 16 year old)**

Whose responsibility?

What happens if you're one of the unlucky ones and home tuition is not forthcoming. Who is responsible?

As previously mentioned, the Local Education Authority (LEA) is responsible, even if your school is grant maintained.

"The practical effect of section 298 of the Education Act 1993 is that, from its coming into force in September 1994, all LEAs will be obliged to arrange suitable education for all children of compulsory school age who are out of school because of illness or injury."

(The Education of Sick Children. Cir. 12/94 para 16)

Persistence may be needed in the early stages if home tuition is not looking very likely. Your name needs to be continually on the top of the 'in tray' at County Hall. Your parents need to keep calm, formal but persistent and they need to keep the letters flowing. They could ask at your school for the name of the Education Officer dealing with Special Needs at County Hall and arrange for a personal visit. Face to face communication is usually so much more productive than telephone calls.

A member of the local ME support group may be willing to go with your parents. They can take on the role of informant as far as the illness is concerned, allowing your parents to put the carer's situation.

When things get slowed up or blocked altogether between parents and the authorities it is intensely frustrating but all parties need to remain calm. Another one of the family members might like to take up the case, allowing the first family member a respite from it all and a cooling off period. The Advisory Centre for Education (ACE) is very familiar with the problems that ME causes and can be contacted for advice (see Useful Addresses). Their booklet 'Children out of School' is useful.

Examinations

The home tutor should be willing to liaise with your school, a point that is particularly important at exam times.

> *"Continuity of work is more likely to be assured where the home tutor liaises with the child's school. This is most important for children at certain stages; for example those at school transfer and those preparing for examinations."*
> *(Education of Sick Children. 12/94 para 69)*

If the request is made early enough, the examination board

may agree to you taking the exam at home with the home tutor.

"All of his exams will be taken at home, I only needed to ask and the school's examination's officer did the rest. Stefan will have his home tutor invigilating for most of them and will be able to rest when he wants to. For his ten hour Art exam I had to keep a timetable showing exactly when he started and stopped painting. As he did this in half hour blocks, I was able to invigilate, providing I kept a timetable. They knew it to be his own work as they could see his painting style from his course work.

He managed to complete his piece in four days (at school they have two days)."   (Carer of 16 year old)

You may be making good progress at the moment, maybe even studying back at school/college like Victoria below. You probably feel that you will be able to take the examinations with everyone else but to request a home examination in the first instance is best. It cuts out on the tiring travel to and from school and allows your brain to concentrate on the knowledge in your head rather than the pain in your legs or back.

"Victoria had little rest at Christmas because of the mock exams, and even less in the Easter holidays because of completing course work. In the Spring she took an Art exam over four mornings which involved a fair amount of standing. She suffered a relapse which meant a four week stay in bed. Then the main exams were on top of us, meaning that she had missed out on the final revision lessons at school.

At that point we wished we had had the foresight to ask for the exams to be taken at home."

(Carer of 16 year old)

If the exam boards turn down the request for home examinations then your parents should ask for provision for you to sit the exam in a quiet room and be allowed to rest when you need to. To sit in a sports' hall for over an hour on a hard chair, is a very stressful experience and only a patient well into the Recovery stage would be able to take the pressure without chancing a relapse.

Returning to school

Like everything else, returning to school must be taken gradually. The ideal start would be for you to join in your favourite lesson, once a week; Art on a Tuesday afternoon, for example. The middle of the day is often the best time, when you feel at the peak of your energy - little though that is!

Gradually, that one afternoon can be extended to include registration and then some of the lunch hour. Don't push too quickly but don't be frightened to try a little more if there is no adverse reaction.

In some areas the Home Tutor will be prepared to accompany you into the classroom and give you assistance. In art, for example, they could do all the walking about, collecting equipment etc.

Most senior schools have a department for Special Educational Needs. These departments often have quiet rooms for study and can arrange for integration into the mainstream to happen slowly. They are not just in school to help pupils with learning to read, they are there for students with special needs. You have a need for quiet and carefully organised integration.

Once you have built up some time in school, you should begin to think in terms of following one subject. It is less tiring to concentrate on one subject and go into school on several days, for just one lesson, than to attend for one whole morning and cover several subjects.

Continuity is important and by following one subject you are able to keep up with the rest of the class. You are not left in a continual state of catching up with information that you missed on days when you didn't attend. My suggestion, then, is to build up subject by subject rather than day by day.

Post-16 Education

Once you are passed the age of sixteen years you can breathe easier, in that the pressure of having to attend school is lifted. The down side of this is that if you are trying to catch up on the missed years, the local education authority may only be prepared to fund a school's sixth form attendance. Sixth Form *colleges* do not all come under the same funding arrangement as the schools.

Most sixth forms, nowadays have GCSE or GNVQ courses available but there are still some schools that will only run 'A' levels. The qualifications needed for these are GCSEs, which you may have missed.

It is worth shopping around to different schools and colleges to get the course that you want. GNVQs (General National Vocational Qualifications) are modular - passed in blocks of learning rather than a two or three year course. The Foundation level GNVQ is particularly useful if you have missed a great deal of Years 10 and 11 because it starts fairly simple and finishes around GCSE level 'C/D'. If this course is too easy for you, then the next level will be available for you.

Often the colleges are happy for you to take just a few modules and take the rest the following year. Your local careers bureau will be able to help you find the right course.

Further Education

F.E. colleges are often more flexible in their courses than a school's sixth form, especially regarding the time of day that they run, but these can be costly. This is where it is useful to have built up a fund from any benefits that you may qualify for. Adult education courses, which are usually run in the evening, are sometimes held at your local school which may be easier for you to get to. Again your local careers office will hold the information.

Open Learning Schemes

These are run by local colleges and are a boon to those of you who cannot yet get out much.

To join, one enrols at the college and is assigned a personal tutor who assists you as you need it. I've heard of two schemes where the tutor comes to the house, so do ask. During the tutorial, work is assigned for you to complete as and when you feel capable - a real boon!

This form of learning is usually charged by the hour, an average figure seeming to be between £10-£15 for the tutorial and marking the work.

Open University

The most famous open learning facility is the Open University. One only has to be over 18 years of age and wish to study. No entry qualifications are needed so lack of 'A' levels or GCSEs is no handicap. To ensure a slower, more gradual start, it may be preferable to start with a short, single course. Many of these courses count towards a final degree, should you wish to continue.

Although tutorials are held at local centres it is not obligatory for you to attend. Some tutors will even visit the sufferer's home instead. It is possible to be excused from Summer School if suffering from ME, and you may be offered extended time for writing assignments and for taking exams.

The courses are not cheap and, although part time courses are not usually funded, it is worth approaching your Local Authority for a grant, Special consideration is sometimes given to persons with disability, so it is worth trying.

The Useful Addresses section at the end of this book will give you the address of your local area OU office. The ME Association has a support group for OU students and it might be worth contacting them for any further information.

"I send out details of how the OU helps students with ME and offer a few names of others with similar study interests.

When the going gets tough, it's helpful to contact other ME sufferers who are studying with the OU. I don't circulate ages or telephone numbers, it isn't a dating agency. It's a support for the isolation that you sometimes feel, together with the lack of self esteem."

(OU support group co-ordinator. ME Association)

Correspondence Colleges

These are often advertised in newspapers and magazines and include names such as NEC (National Extension College) and CACC (Council for the Accreditation of Correspondence Courses) - see Useful Addresses.

The courses that they offer are varied: academic, professional or leisure. It is a good idea to write to the CACC for the names of approved colleges before you apply. Remember that anyone can set themselves up as a training 'college' and even state that they are accredited. Check it out before handing over your money as they are often expensive.

Full Time Higher Education

If you are well enough to go to university or college full time, I can recommend a booklet published by Skill : National Bureau for Students with Disabilities - see Useful Addresses. The booklet, 'Higher Education and Disability' names many universities and colleges which have special arrangements for disabled students. It explains how you apply for the courses and whether you are eligible for funding.

The National Bureau itself provides a range of leaflets with information on grants, allowances, benefits and trusts, and can provide you with individual advice on both higher and further education.

In general, I have found that higher educational establishments seem to be able to give more support and are more understanding of the limitations of ME than are the schools.

Once you feel up to it, I think that taking some form of course or learning a new skill, is very beneficial. It certainly gets the 'ferry boats' chugging around again (see Chapter 5) and it says a lot about your self determination. It is impressive to show that, despite a long-term illness, you have not only worked to get better but studied bit by bit to fill in the years of limited or thwarted academic study.

15

View From The Top

In the last few chapters, you were given tips on climbing the mountain. Like all good mountaineers, I think you would now like to read of others that have already reached the top. Not so easy as it may appear! Plenty of young people have managed it but they are reluctant to talk about it.

Try getting a real mountaineer or intrepid explorer to tell you of his or her exploits once they have returned. They'll tell you of their future plans, how wonderful it was to see their family again after the climb and they might mention how great the view was from the top of the mountain. The rest is left to any available video or film footage. Somehow, when something great is achieved through adversity or hardship, it isn't easy to re-live it. "Oh it was nothing", is the usual conversation stopper.

Similarly, I found it difficult to track down young people who would talk about their recovery from ME. They had pushed away the memories of that pathway in their life and were now busy building new ones. They didn't want to return to the mountain.

I was very lucky, therefore, that Kerry and Anna were prepared to share their stories with me. Kerry contracted ME when she was 14 years old, Anna when she was 19 years. They both spent the first year of their illness battling against the symptoms of ME, prejudice and disbelief. They too found the trees in the forest and had to come to terms with the limitations that ME brings. They have climbed the mountain, had their slips and falls and struggled back again. I am pleased to say that both of them have now recovered to 95% on the Ability Scale and are picking up on life with great gusto.

Kerry

Three years ago, Kerry had sent her story to the teenage magazine, MIZZ. They covered her story in a sympathetic and well informed manner. At that time she had just been diagnosed as having ME after battling with unsympathetic doctors for over a year. When I reminded Kerry of how poorly she had been, by sending her a copy of the article she was rather shocked:

"Was I really that ill?"

Like many successful achievers, Kerry was reluctant to talk about her experiences. However, she was happy for parts of the magazine article to be published to show all young people currently in a similar position, that recovery is round the corner.

While you are reading, try to spot the DRAGS emotions. They are not crystal clear because at the time of being interviewed for the article she had already reached the stage of acceptance. The last paragraph shows this very clearly. The shared memories from Kerry's mum shows how the whole family have been through the forest and up the mountain with her. Through talking together they became united as a family.

> *"It all started in the December. I began to feel sick all the time. Everything was becoming a massive effort. I realised that there was something wrong but thought I*

would get over it in time. Soon after that I got very bad 'flu and felt as though I was going to die. I was only fourteen but I lay there in bed thinking - this is it, I'm on my way out.

I never really recovered from that but I tried to get back to school. It didn't work. I kept having to come home again because of the awful pains I had in my stomach. It was like I had been beaten up. It felt as though someone had punched and kicked me every time I ate something. The doctor told me it was a virus and it would clear up.
It didn't.
It was becoming an effort to move and even thinking used up too much energy.

In the summer I watched my friends go off swimming or to Alton Towers for the day. I would have loved to do that - or even just hang around in the park with my mates. I used to think they're all getting boyfriends now and here I am stuck in the house. Even going to the supermarket with my mum would be brilliant - I'd get to see all the things they advertise on the telly.
After the summer I couldn't make it back to classes. My friends didn't understand. I had been the girl who was always going out, often leaving the house at six in the morning to go to horse shows, not getting home 'til ten at night. I was a shadow of my former self having lost two and a half stone in about six months.

After a while I had a home tutor for three half hour sessions every week. That brought a whole new set of problems because I couldn't really concentrate and hold information. It was very demoralising for me as I had been considered bright at school and was in the top sets.

I was sent to a paediatrician who agreed that it was a virus but he couldn't say what kind. He suggested to my mum that perhaps I should see a psychiatrist. I knew that my illness wasn't 'all in the mind'. It wasn't made up. No one could imagine that they felt as awful as I did. I mean there were days when I could hardly stand up.

Still, at last we have a name for my illness - ME. I know now that I'm not going mad.

I know I've missed out on a lot but hopefully I'll get over this soon and I'll want to go out all the time when my friends are beginning to settle down. OK, so I've missed out on all the pressures of exams but I'm going to have to do them one day and hopefully that won't be too far away.

They say it will take time - some people have had ME for ten years - but I never give up hope that I'll be back to normal."

Two and a half years after Kerry had written this she was taking three 'A' Levels and having a very full social life! She would have liked to take on a Saturday job as well but realised that the weekends would be better spent resting and seeing her friends, as the evenings were taken up with homework.

At the time of writing the article above she was 40%, although while she had been fighting the illness and the medical profession one year earlier, she was at 30%.

By looking at the Ability Scale - Chapter 3 and Appendix - you can see that one doesn't go from 30% - 95% overnight. Kerry improved slowly over the years, gradually building up her physical and mental energy levels, taking on more and more studying and enjoying more and more social life.

Kerry's mother takes up the story:

"The first six months were the most difficult. I felt alone in my corner, fighting everyone, with no support. I had no help or guidance from the family GP. My sceptical husband found it easier to cope with being a member of the 'pull yourself together' brigade. One set of grandparents didn't want to know and the other set was too far away to be of any help. My son was puzzled and confused whilst my daughter was getting worse day by day.

I began to read everything and anything on health and ME. With patience and talking together our family grew to understand the illness and one another; we became united and learned to take one day at a time.

The experience has certainly brought us all closer together. Kerry and I in particular as we used to spend hours and hours talking about life.

She and her brother also have a very special bond. He was her lifeline with the outside world.

Physically she has benefitted from Reflexology and Homeopathy, learning the importance of looking after one's self and eating a healthy diet.

Emotionally she has come out of all this a better person, more sympathetic and understanding towards others.

Kerry is enjoying life so much now, she looks upon ME as a hurdle which life presented and one that she has overcome."

At the time of Kerry's article, one year after she was first ill, her daily timetable was printed in the MIZZ magazine article as follows:

10.30am: Wake up and contemplate getting out of bed. Mum goes off to work and I'm left in the house by myself. One of the biggest problems for me is that I'm here alone all day with no one to talk to and not much to do.

11.00am: I literally have to go back to bed to recover from the exertion of getting up and having my breakfast.

11.30am: Get up for the second time and watch TV. Count the minutes until mum comes home for lunch.

12.30am: Mum back to work and I'm alone again. I'll do a jigsaw or play with the rabbit or something. Sometimes I use the computer but that hurts my eyes. I might have a short sleep if I'm very tired. Tutor comes three times a week for just half an hour. I can't concentrate for any longer.

6pm: The rest of the family are back from work or school and we have our dinner. I usually have something a bit different from them as I can't eat a lot of the things they like. I'd do anything for fish and chips or some Chinese.

6.30pm: Spend the rest of the evening watching TV or have some of my friends round. I never have much to say to them but they keep me up with the gossip from school.

9.30pm: Off to bed again. Sometimes I suffer from insomnia and have to get up during the night because I can't sleep. I'm very tired and want to sleep but somehow I just can't.

Two years later she had returned to school part-time. During the August school holidays she filled in an Activity Diary for me:

THURS: Woke at 8.45 - 9 hours sleep
Laid in bed 2 hrs.
Aerobics workout ½ hr
2 mile cycle ride ½ hr
Out with friends 2½ hrs, home for tea.
Out with friends 5hrs
Bed at 11pm.

Six months further on and Kerry was studying full time at sixth form college, taking three 'A' levels. A hurried timetable from her stated:

9am - 5 pm: Monday to Friday - Sixth Form studying three 'A' Levels.
Evening: Homework
Weekends: Resting, Socialising, Homework.

The brief note above shows that normality is waiting around the corner for you all.

*   *   *

Anna

Anna's ME started when she was 19 years old. She had just embarked upon her nursing career. I had known Anna indirectly as I had taught her brother at the local Comprehensive school. I was his Form Tutor and he had told me of this strange illness that his sister was suffering from; one that had paralysed her legs but I had no personal knowledge of it and couldn't help him.

Knowing that Anna had now recovered, I asked her to write down her thoughts of how she had managed to survive and recover. However, she had been suffering from ME for five years - a hugh project to write about. Besides this, like many other survivors of ME, she found writing it all down very difficult, despite the fact that she desperately wanted to share it with you.

"It's so difficult to write down just how awful you've been and what mistakes you've made. You don't want to admit that it really was you that was spoon fed and toileted. A bit like Post Traumatic Stress, perhaps. You shut it out, or perhaps you don't even take it all in in the first place. You need all your spare energy just existing."

We decided therefore that I would interview Anna. She could tell me about it even if she couldn't write it down.

You will see from what follows, that throughout Anna's recovery period she shows a strong determination to be well. Certainly there is a great deal of Denial in the early stages and this may have lengthened her recovery period. The 'Return' tree is one that has almost followed her up the mountain and one that she still fights off, even today. She believes that by accepting ME, one accepts that the trees are always going to appear when you least expect them to. They may not be the same large and foreboding trees that you identified in the original forest but they have the same names and whenever or wherever you bump into them, they can still hurt.

Anna's story starts some seven years ago.

"It was June. I was at college, about to take some extra 'O' levels, when a virus struck. My legs were paralysed; I couldn't walk. I was absolutely devastated as I was a county athlete and ran daily.

It took six weeks to recover from this virus and during this time I had to take my exams. Mum took me into the exam room in a wheelchair where I spent the first ten minutes crying over the paper. I felt absolutely dreadful.

After my exams I worked full time in a supermarket. I hadn't really recovered from this virus. I could walk but I was still in a lot of pain and very tired. I was due to start my nursing career at the end of the year so I desperately needed some money. I worked 40-50 hours a week! One day I had such pain in my chest that I dropped a whole tray of Baked Beans that I was carrying and they rolled everywhere.

In August I finally started my nursing but within weeks I caught a gastroenteritis bug that was rife in the hospital. I never really recovered from that. I couldn't understand why I couldn't shake of this awful fatigue. Day by day the hospital corridors seemed longer and longer. I convinced myself that it was the new job/shift work/pace of nursing that was doing it.

I thought I must be very unfit. So I decided on an intense fitness regime. I would come home from work, then go and play badminton and then go swimming.

Of course, it didn't help at all, it just made things a whole lot worse. I would pass out by the patients' beds. I had never felt so awful. I wanted the patients to move over in bed so that I could climb in!

The muscles around my mouth dropped and I couldn't speak properly. The words came out all slurry. I couldn't even say what I was thinking. I'd go up to the ward sister with a really important thing to say, open my mouth and out would come: 'Chair!'

I'd think - What? Where did that come from?

Each day it got worse. I'd go home, slump on the couch and not be able to move or eat.

I was going to the doctor's every week, trying ever stronger antibiotics. My poor immune system didn't stand a chance to sort itself out on its own. I had tried everything to get better, intensive exercise, ignoring it, working it off. Nothing had worked.

By the end of the year, ME was diagnosed and I had to give up my career.

The doctor who diagnosed my illness was very good. He took an hour to talk to me about ME but I guess I only picked out what I wanted to hear. I decided that ME meant that I would be ill every now and then. The reason why I would have to give up nursing was because my health was unreliable."

Over the next 6 - 8 months Anna became progressively worse as she slid down the Ability Scale to 0%. She was sharing a house with her boyfriend who had to do everything for her. The house was hardly suitable for someone suffering from ME - it had three storeys!

"In the early afternoon, I'd shuffle along to the bathroom on my bottom, and using the same mode of transport eventually get downstairs. It took ages to get down there but at least I could see some greenery from the lounge. I never stayed in bed because I could only see next door's wall from there, it was so depressing.

Once I got downstairs, I stayed on the sofa until my boyfriend came home to piggy back me upstairs again to the bathroom and my bed.

A year after I became ill, in the July, we moved to a ground floor flat and I finally decided that a wheelchair would be a good thing to have. I was in the most dreadful pain when we went out but at least I felt part of the outside world again."

Anna became an active member of the local ME group and became interested in counselling. She started to run successful workshops, giving other sufferers support. In addition she was attempting to have a social life. I asked her whether she felt that this was over doing it a bit.

"Oh definitely, without a doubt, I did far too much. There were far too many times when I found myself in situations that I didn't want to be in, feeling absolutely dreadful. It was because I was always thinking of other people.

I felt a kind of responsibility to go out when others wanted to. It took me years to say, 'No - I'd rather stay on my own'.

I didn't honour myself enough to stay at home when I should have done."

I asked Anna whether she felt this 'Return' attitude - needing to be the same as others - had lengthened her illness. This was a difficult question for her and she finally answered from a different tack.

> *"My boyfriend would say, 'Yes, definitely'. He was always sitting me down and telling me to rest but it was like banging his head against a brick wall. I wouldn't listen. I just wanted to be normal; to do everything that everybody else was doing. I don't think I've ever accepted that I can't go back and start again."*

She told me that despite feeling very poorly she would go to the supermarket in the wheelchair. I found it difficult to understand why she had chosen to drain her limited energy in such a stressful atmosphere.

> *"But it was such an empowering thing to do - choose your own food! I'd push the trolley in front of me, hardly able to see over the top saying, 'One of those, two of those...'."*

Mentally, Anna was feeling able to tackle a little more. She was working hard for the local ME Support Group but felt she needed something extra.

> *"I was so desperate to do something more than run the local ME group that, in the winter I signed up for the Open University. I was probably at 40% able and it meant writing an essay every month. It was ridiculous really.*
> *I'd drive to the tutorial - right up to the door - and then, because I was so desperate for some social interaction,*

*I'd go to the pub with others afterwards. They thought
it very strange that I had to drive the 80 yards down the
road, in order to be right outside the door again."*

Very, very gradually, Anna began to make progress. With each
stage of recovery she added more interests, studying at
Further Education college and finally a course at University.

There were ups and downs in her health, including one very
serious relapse. She was taken into hospital where she was
badgered by doctors and nurses to exercise every day and
generally to pull herself together. The more she articulated
about the limitations of ME, the more she was disbelieved.

However, by discussing her illness in detailed terms she was
able to see for herself why the relapse may have occurred.

*"It was an accumulative effect, I think. Instead of
adding more and more activities every time I felt a little
better, I should have used the extra energy that I was
feeling to help my immune system sort itself out. My
boyfriend used to ask me if I really knew what I was
doing to myself. I wasn't saving any energy to heal, just
rushing around trying to live my life to the full. I don't
think I realised that ME had already filled it!*

*This relapse made me finally realise what I was doing.
From that time I began to have regular rests in the
afternoon, even when I felt well. I called it my 'Active
Rest' and I immediately began to feel much better for
it. I was still determined to get better but it became a
much more planned approach. A bit like your Base
Camp, I suppose.*

I began to take care of myself. My 'active rest' became as necessary to my personal care as brushing my teeth and having a shower; as important to the day as getting dressed or washing the dishes."

Although Anna was now taking care of herself physically, she was frustrated that life appeared to be passing her by too quickly.

"I was in such a panic to catch up really quick. I wanted to do everything 'now' because everyone else was doing it. I didn't think I would have any time later."

At one of the ME support meetings Anna met an older lady. She explained to Anna that life would wait and things did not have to all be done 'today'.

"This lady told me that life slows at 30 years and suddenly you realise that you have plenty of time to do all the things that you've ever wanted to do. I hadn't realised that. I thought that the older you got the less time you have. Thinking about this I realised that you don't have to catch up as such, it all happens indirectly."

Over the next two to three years, Anna recovered and trained as a Play Therapist for children with chronic illnesses and trauma, spending some time working in America. She had obviously been devastated when she realised that the rigours of a nursing career were not going to mix with ME but the new opportunities that she had found enabled her to use her talents and experiences to the full. Her recovery filled her with euphoria.

"I was so happy to be me, so lucky to have got so far up the mountain. You'll never believe how many shoes I wore out. I just walked and walked. My friends would catch a bus or drive to places in their cars but I'd say, 'I'll see you there', and walk! All weathers, it didn't matter, I was just so proud of myself.

I could walk side by side with my boyfriend instead of being pushed in the wheelchair. You can't hold hands when you're being pushed! I could walk arm in arm like all the other young couples."

These were obviously very happy and satisfying times for Anna. She was working part time, studying, enjoying a social life, taking care of herself and walking everywhere!

This was still insufficient for her as she missed her running.

"Even after all those years I missed my running, so my boyfriend came out jogging with me. First I could only manage 30 seconds, then 45 seconds - 5 minutes - 10 - 15. It was very painful though but I was determined to push on.

I was stupid really because I'd been thriving on walking everywhere, really enjoying myself, why did I need to run? Plus I wanted to get into full time work."

As a play therapist, Anna landed a job working in a leading London hospital. We arranged to meet and discuss her part in this book as soon as she had settled into her new post.

Three weeks after starting her job she contracted viral meningitis. This was devastating news, not only for Anna but for everyone who knew her. I expected her to be thrown right back after such a serious illness but two months later she made the train journey to Milton Keynes to meet with me. She looked remarkably well and put her ability level at 70%. You will not be surprised that this level was not good enough for Anna.

> *"Oh I'd expected to be back to work by now. My consultant said that I might need 6 - 9 months convalescence after meningitis but I'm hoping to return part time very soon."*

I told her to think very carefully about pacing herself slowly and evenly; reminded her of the plans she had made at her Base Camp when she was suffering from ME.

> *"Yes, I know. Underneath I always think I can return to my pre-ME path, it keeps me going."*

A few weeks later, I phoned Anna to find that she had thought carefully about pacing herself and with the hospital withdrawing their support of her, she had very sensibly handed in her notice.

ME had taught her how to take care of herself after a viral illness and this would assist her recovery from meningitis. It is a lesson that we can all take with us through life.

Anna's recent illness rather clouds the recovery that she made from ME and I was very tempted to leave it out, finishing on the euphoria of 'walking everywhere'. However, life is not that simple. Just because we have recovered from ME, we are just as susceptible to catching other viruses. Until the medical world can come up with a definite reason for getting ME, it may be that we are *more* susceptible to viral illnesses.

$$*\qquad\qquad*\qquad\qquad*$$

Kerry and Anna are two young people who have climbed the mountain, learned about taking care of themselves and are now living normal lives. Adding to their studies slowly, bit by bit, often through home study, they have shown that it is possible to study for 'A' levels and a degree and be ready to use them when the time is right.

       *   *   *

In reading this book, and these two stories in particular, I hope that you have found:

* You are not alone with how you're feeling at present.

* That other young people have seen the trees in the forest.

* There is hope for the future.

Never give up hope. Both Kerry and Anna have been ill for longer than the average figure of four years. Because of this I was able to get hold of them easily and their stories were noteworthy. The many young people who have been ill for a much shorter time were far more difficult to contact but they are out there!

Remember that everyone is different. There is no correlation between how far you have slipped down the Ability Scale and how long it will take you to climb up it again. Each person's route through the forest and up the mountain will be different. However, some things will remain the same.

The symptoms and T-R-U-S-T, the comprehensive treatment plan, is the same for everyone. The trees of emotion may change in size and severity but most people, regardless of age, will meet at least some of them at some time.

*   *   *

The forest is a right DRAG but a necessary part of leaving one pathway and using another for a time. TRUST this new pathway as it will almost certainly be your lifeline for many months to come. It will lead you to the BASE CAMP where you can rest until you are able to build up your activity.

Climb carefully over the mountain and don't be discouraged by set-backs. You, like many others, will succeed in the end.

Good Luck

and

Keep Smiling

Appendix

Diagnostic
Criteria

and

Young Person's
Ability Scale

DIAGNOSTIC CRITERIA FOR CHILDREN
(Task Force Report)

To be given a diagnosis of CFS the child must score 12 or more points from the list below.

Abnormal fatigue **must** be present.

* **Abnormal Fatigue -** to include (a) along with 2 others from (b)(c)(d)(e)

  (a) physical exhaustion which comes on within 12 hours of doing fairly simple activity and takes 24-72 hours to recover
  (b) exhausted but wanting to do more
  (c) waking from a night's sleep feeling exhausted
  (d) exhaustion accompanied by feeling unwell
  (e) tiredness or exhaustion which is made worse by any further infections such as the common cold.
  Score [5]

* Sudden onset which started with a feverish illness and/or sore throat and/or lymph glands enlargement (neck/armpit/groin). **Score [2]**

* Muscle pain and/or tenderness. **Score [2]**

* Severe headaches which are not fully relieved by simple painkillers. **Score [2]**

* Disturbance of temperature control (cold feet and hands with rest of the body feeling warm). **Score [2]**

* Pins and needles / Feeling of being touched / Muscle twitching / Long term hiccup / Weakness or paralysis in fingers, hands or feet / Dizziness or feeling of losing one's balance (vertigo).
Score [1] for each, using a maximum of 2 items

* Disturbance of memory / Difficulty with concentration / Inability to name common objects or calling objects by the wrong name
Score [1] for each, using a maximum of 2 items

* Eye pain or blurring of vision after reading for more than 10 minutes / Oversensitivity to light / Oversensitivity to noise.
Score [1] for each, using a maximum of 2 items

* Sleep pattern which is different from normal and on-going, day after day. **Score [1]**

* Severe chest or tummy pains for most of the day over at least a month. **Score [1]**

* Persistent change of bowel habit. Diarrhoea or constipation which is constant and different from normal. **Score [1]**

* Standing still is considerably more tiring than walking. **Score [1]**

This scoring system was devised by Dr David Lewis, consultant paediatrician in Aberystwyth. It is published in its complete form in the 1994 Task Force Report to the Department of Health, available from Westcare (see Useful Addresses).

YOUNG PERSON'S ABILITY SCALE

100%   No symptoms even following physical or mental exertion. Able to study full time without difficulty, plus enjoy a social life.

95%   No symptoms at rest. Mild symptoms following physical or mental exertion - tire rather easily but fully recovered next day. Able to study full time without difficulty but it means a slight restriction on social life.

90%   No symptoms at rest. Mild symptoms following physical or mental exertion - tire easily. Study full time with some difficulty. Social life rather restricted.

80%   Mild symptoms at rest, worsened by physical or mental exertion. Full time study at school or college difficult, especially if it is a crowded, noisy environment. Home tuition or part-time study without difficulty.

70%   Mild symptoms at rest, worsened by physical or mental exertion. Daily activity limited. Part time study at school/college tiring, restricting social life. With home study and careful pacing of activities, some social life is possible. Careful exercise may be possible: walking/swimming/cycling.

60%   Mild to moderate symptoms at rest. Increasing symptoms following physical or mental exertion. Daily activity very limited, although gentle walking/swimming/cycling is possible. Unable to study with others. Short (1 or 2 hours) daily home study is possible. Quiet, non-active social life possible.

50%   Moderate symptoms at rest. Increasing symptoms following physical or mental exertion. Regular rest periods needed. Simple, short home study possible when alternated with quiet, non-active social life. Not confined to the house but unable to walk much further than 200yds. Enjoy a trip to the shops in the wheelchair.

40% Moderate symptoms at rest. Moderate to severe symptoms following physical or mental exertion. Not confined to the house but unable to walk much more than 100 yds. Can manage a wheelchair outing to the shops on a quiet day. Requires three or four regular rest periods during the day. Only one large activity possible per day - friend dropping by or doctor's visit or short home study, etc. Rest of the time spent pottering around.

30% Moderate to severe symptoms at rest with possible weakness in hands and arms. Severe symptoms following any physical or mental exertion. Usually confined to the house but enjoy a quiet wheelchair ride or a gentle walk in the fresh air. Most of the day resting, although some small tasks possible (e.g. letter writing). Mental concentration poor and home study very difficult indeed.

20% Fairly severe symptoms at rest. Weakness in hands, arms or legs may be restricting movement. Unable to leave the house except rarely. Confined to bed/settee most of the day but able to sit in a chair for short periods. Unable to concentrate for more than one hour a day.

10% Severe symptoms at rest. In bed the majority of the time. No travel outside the house. Concentration very difficult indeed.

0% Severe symptoms on a continuous basis. In bed constantly. Unable to sit up. Unable to care for yourself.

Useful Addresses

ME Associations

ME Association
Stanhope House
High Street
Stanford-le-Hope
Essex
SS17 0HA
Tel: 01375 642466
Information Line: 01375 361013 1.30pm to 4pm
ME Association will give the addresses of the Young People's Group, together with the Open University Study Group.

C.F.S Foundation
52 St Enoch Square
Glasgow
G1 4AA
Tel: 0141 2043822

Action for ME
PO Box 1302
Wells
Somerset
BA5 2WE
Tel: 01749 670799

Westcare
155 Whiteladies Road
Clifton
Bristol
BS8 2RF
Tel: 0117 9239341

Main service is to the south west of England where a clinic in Bristol provides consultations with professional advisers/counsellors. Task Force Report available from Westcare.

National ME Support Centre
Disablement Services Centre
Harold Wood Hospital
Romford
Essex
RM3 9AR
Tel: 01708 378050

Facilities for both in-patient and out-patient care. The centre offers counselling (medical and non-medical) for patients with a firm diagnosis of ME

Education

Advisory Centre for Education (ACE)
1B Aberdeen Studios
22-24 Highbury Grove
London
N5 2DQ
Tel: 0171 3548318
Advice Service: 0171 3548321 2pm to 5pm

"Helping parents support their children in school."

Council for the Accreditation of Correspondence Colleges (CACC)
27 Marylebone road
London NW1 5JS
Tel: 0171 9355391

National Extension College (NEC)
18 Brooklands Ave
Cambridge CB2 2HN
Tel: 01223 316644

Education Otherwise

PO Box 120
Leamington Spa
Warwickshire
CV32 7ER

"A self-help organisation which can offer support, advice and information to families practicing or contemplating home-based education as an alternative to schooling."

National Association for the Education of Sick Children

18 Victoria Park Square
London
E2 9PF
Tel: 0181 9808523

"Working for every child's right to education when they are sick."

Open University

Central Enquiry Service
PO Box 200
Walton Hall
Milton Keynes MK7 6YZ
Tel: 01908 653231

Open College

FREEPOST
Warrington
WA2 7BR

Skill : National Bureau for Students with Disabilities

336 Brixton Road
London SW9 7AA
Tel: 0171 2740565 Advice line 2pm-5pm weekdays

Benefits

Benefit Enquiry Line for people with disabilities and their carers.
Freephone: 0800 882200 8am to 6.30pm Mon-Fri
9am to 1pm Sat

Freeline Social Security gives general advice about Social Security benefits and National Insurance contributions:
Freephone: 0800 666 555

DLA Central Enquiry Handling Service is for advice on existing DLA claims: 0345 123 456 (local rate)

Incapacity Benefit Leaflet Line supplies leaflets on request: Freephone: 0800 868 868

Benefits Agency
Quarry House
Quarry Hill
Leeds
LS2 7UA

Support Services

Crossroads Care Attendant Schemes
10 Regent Place
Rugby
Warwickshire
CU21 2PN
Tel: 01788 573653
"Offers practical help for families with a disabled member."

Dial UK
Park Lodge
St Catherine's Hospital
Tickhill Road
Balby
Doncaster
S. Yorks
DN4 8QN
Tel: 01302 310123

"Headquarters of a network of 100 disability advice centres."

Disabled Living Foundation
380-384 Harrow Road
London
W9 2HU

"Provides practical, up-to-date advice and information on all aspects of living with disability for disabled people and their carers."

Disability Law Service
16 Princeton Street
London
WC1R 4BR
Tel: 0171 8318031

"Provides free legal advice to people with disabilities and their carers. They specialise in benefits, education and employment, and can offer free representation at appeals and make home visits."

RADAR
12 City Forum
250 City Road
London
EC1V 8AF
Tel: 0171 2503222

"Information on mobilty, access, social services, employment, housing, holidays."

Counselling Services

Sunbow Postal Counselling Services
Sunbow House
5 Medland
Woughton Park
Milton Keynes
MK6 3BH
Tel: 01908 691635

"Provides postal counselling for young people with ME, based on the ideas covered in this book."

Youth Access
Magazine Business Centre
11 Newarke Street
Leicester LE1 5SS

"Provides a national referral service for all young people to their local advice and counselling service."

Respite Care

ME Association provides a leaflet on Respite Care.

Travel

Holiday Care Service
2 Old Bank Chambers
Station Road
Horley
Surrey
RG6 9HW
Tel: 01293 774535

"Central resource on information about holidays for disabled people."

Youth Organisations

Action for Children
85 Highbury Park
London
N5 1UD
Tel: 0171 2262033

"Runs over 200 projects throughout the UK which include family centres and disability projects."

National Council for Voluntary Youth Services
Coborn House
Coborn Road
London
E3 2DA
Tel: 0181 9805712

"NCVYS can help you to find an appropriate youth organisation anywhere in England."

References

ACE "Children out of school." 1993   *Advisory Centre for Education.*

ACE "Home tuition - who pays?" July 1993 *ACE Bulletin.*

Arnold D.L. et al. "Excessive intracellular acidosis of skelatal muscle on exercise in a patient with Postviral Exhaustion/ Fatigue Syndrome." 1984 *The Lancet i:1367-1369.*

Behan W.M.H. et al. "Mitochondrial abnormalities in the Postviral Fatigue Syndrome." 1991 *Acta Neuropathologica vol 83:61-65.*

Bell D. "CFIDS: A disease of a thousand names". 1991 *Pollard Publications USA.*

Bell D et al. "Primary Juvenile Fibromyalgia Syndrome and CFS in adolescents." 1994   *Clinical Infectious Diseases   vol 18(supp1):21.*

Bell D. "Chronic Fatigue Syndrome in children." in Journal of Chronic Fatigue Syndrome. 1995 *Haworth Press. vol 1,1.*

Carpenter A and Johnson G. "Why am I afraid to grieve?" 1994 *Fount.*

Colby J. "Guidelines for schools." 1993 *Action for ME.*

Collinge W. "Recovering from ME - A guide to self-enpowerment" 1994 *Souvenir Press.*

Cox D and Findley L. "Is CFS treatable in an NHS environment?" 1994 *Clinical Rehabilitation vol 8,1:76-80*.

Department for Education. "The education of sick children." 1994 *DFE Circular No:12/94*.

Dowsett E.G. "Preliminary report of the working party on young people with ME." 1991 *Unpublished*

Ferber R. "Sleep schedule-dependent causes in insomnia and sleep disorders." 1990 *Paediatrician vol 17:13-20*.

Franklin A. "Children with ME - guidelines for school doctors and general practioners." 1995 *ME Association.*

Holmes G.P. "C.F.S: a working case definition." 1988 *Annals of Internal Medicine 108:387-389.*

Horne J. "Why we sleep." *Oxford University Press 1964.*

Ho-Yen D. "Better recovery from viral illness." 1993 *Dodona Books.*

International CFS Study Group. "The Chronic Fatigue Syndrome: a comprehensive approach to its definition and study." 1994 *Annals of Internal Medicine. 121(12):953-959.*

Lane R.J.M et al. "Lactate responses to exercise in Chronic Fatigue Syndrome." 1994 *Journal of Neurology, Neurosurgery and Psychiatry. 57,5:662-3*

Lloyd A, Hickie I et al. "Prevalence of Chronic Fatigue Syndrome in an Australian population." 1990 *Medical Journal of Australia 153:522-528.*

ME Association. "Guidelines for the education of young people with ME." 1992 *ME Association.*

McGarry F et al. "Enterovirus in the Chronic Fatigue Syndrome." 1994 *Annals of Internal Medicine 120,11:972-973.*

Milne A.A. "The Pooh book of quotations." edited by Sibley B. 1986 *Methuen.*

NAESC. "Education for sick children: Directory of current provision in England and Wales." 1994 *National Association for the Education of Sick Children.*

Sharpe M.C et al. "A report - Chronic Fatigue Syndrome: guidelines for research." 1991 *Journal Royal Society Medicine. 84:118-121.*

Shepherd C. "Living with ME." 1992 *Cedar.*

Shepherd C. "Guidelines for the care of patients." 1994 *ME Association.*

Smith D.G. "Understanding ME." 1991 *Robinson.*

Skill: National Bureau for Students with Disabilities. "Higher Education and Disability." 1993 *Hobsons.*

Task Force, The National. "Report on CFS/PVFS/ME." 1994 *Westcare.*

Index

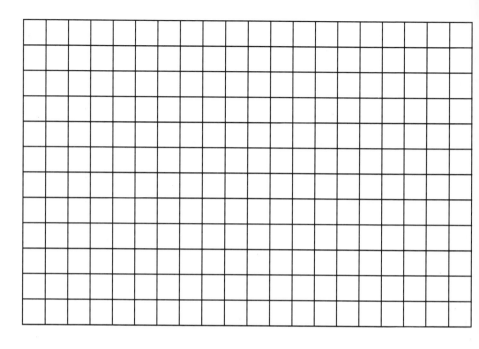

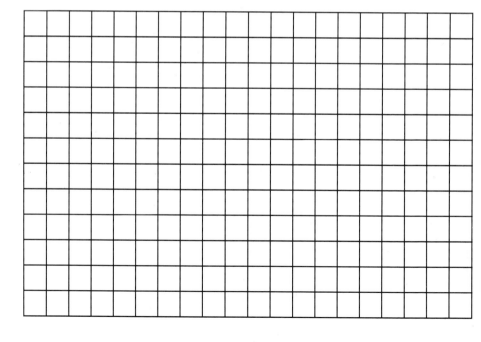

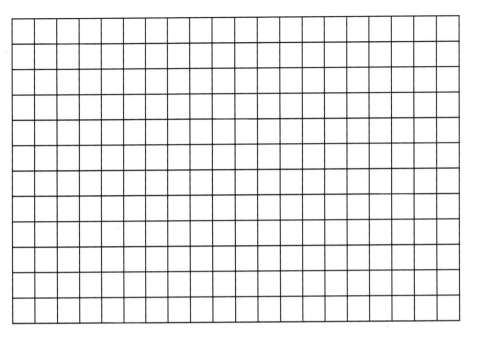

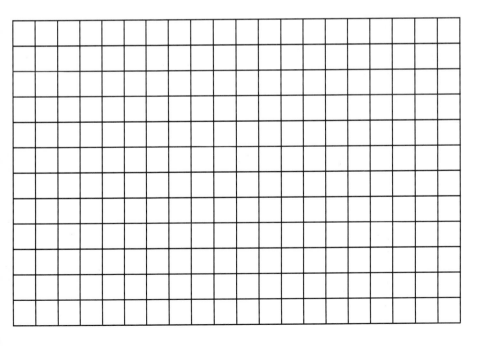

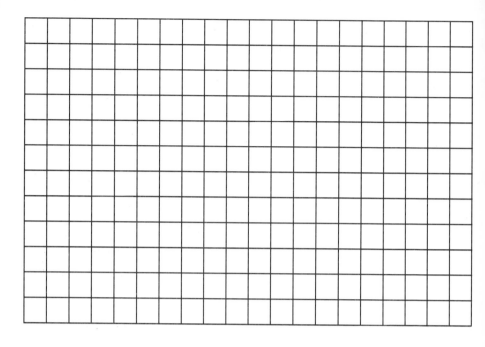

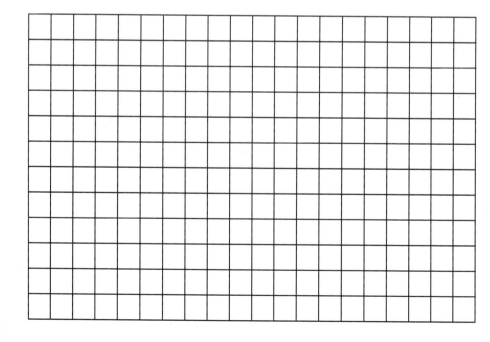

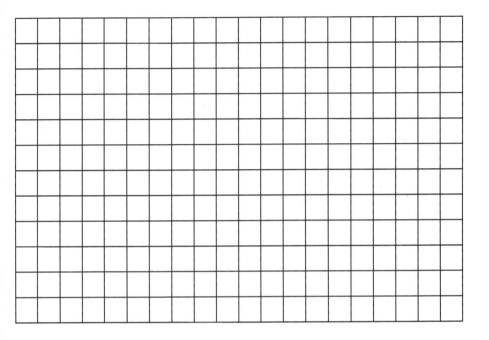

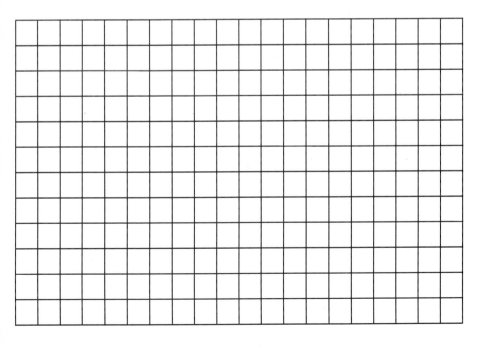